# MODERN NETWORK SYNTHESIS

*Volume 1: APPROXIMATION*

# MODERN NETWORK SYNTHESIS

## Volume 1: *APPROXIMATION*

DONALD A. CALAHAN

Assistant Professor
*Department of Electrical Engineering*
*University of Illinois*

HAYDEN BOOK COMPANY, INC., NEW YORK

a division of HAYDEN PUBLISHING COMPANY, INC.

*Dedicated to*
Loretta and Martha

# PREFACE

This monograph is written to serve as an introduction to the literature in the approximation field. It is directed to anyone who has taken a network synthesis course from one of the standard texts (see Bibliography B1.1) or anyone with an equivalent mathematics and circuits background. It should be useful for both the worker in the filter design field who may wish to up-date his knowledge and the student, who will find, particularly in the problems, an introduction to more stimulating work in the network field. As a text, this monograph could be used to supplement a second course in network synthesis.

The text begins with a discussion of realizability of certain ideal responses, then treats elliptic functions and their optimal approximating properties, and concludes with a chapter on the use of the computer in approximation. Examples are employed throughout, particularly in the discussion of filter design and computer applications.

An extensive bibliography arranged by topic has been added to aid in literature searches.

DONALD A. CALAHAN

*January 1964*
*Berkeley, California*

# CONTENTS

# 1

# INTRODUCTION TO APPROXIMATION

Before proceeding into the actual approximation of certain "ideal" responses with rational functions,† we will review, in this chapter, the properties of the magnitude, delay and phase functions commonly associated with rational network functions. Then we will define the "ideal" responses and discuss their realizability.

## 1.1. Parts of Network Functions

*Magnitude Function.* Let us consider any network function ($z_{12}$, $y_{12}$, etc.) and call it $T(s)$. The squared magnitude, then, of $T(s)$ as a function of $\omega$ is

$$|T(j\omega)|^2 = T(j\omega)\ T^*(j\omega) \qquad (1\text{-}1)$$

$$= T(j\omega)\ T(-j\omega) \qquad (1\text{-}2)$$

Evidently, from Eq. 1-2, $|T(j\omega)|^2$ is a ratio of even polynomials in $\omega$. We now define

$$W(s^2) = |T(j\omega)|^2_{\omega^2 = -s^2} \qquad (1\text{-}3)$$

$$= T(s)\ T(-s) \qquad (1\text{-}4)$$

---

† Ratios of polynomials.

1

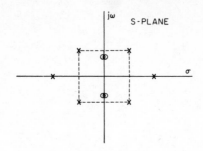

**Fig. 1-1.** Zeros and poles of $W(s^2)$.

Necessary and sufficient conditions that $|T(j\omega)|^2$ be a magnitude (squared) function are then (Fig. 1-1):

1. $W(s^2)$ is an even function of s, and thus has zeros and poles quadrantally spaced.
2. Any zeros or poles on the imaginary axis are of even multiplicity.

*Example 1.1:*

$$|T(j\omega)|^2 = \frac{\omega^2 + 1}{\omega^4 + 4} \qquad (1\text{-}5)$$

$$W(s^2) = \frac{-s^2 + 1}{s^4 + 4} \qquad (1\text{-}6)$$

$$= \frac{(s + 1)(-s + 1)}{(s^2 + 2s + 2)(s^2 - 2s + 2)} \qquad (1\text{-}7)$$

Thus, we have

$$T(s) = \frac{s + 1}{s^2 + 2s + 2}, \quad \frac{1 - s}{s^2 + 2s + 2}, \cdots \qquad (1\text{-}8)$$

The arbitrariness in selection of $T(s)$ can be used to obtain either minimum or non-minimum phase, stable or unstable network functions. The implication of this will be discussed later.

*Phase Function.* We let

$$T(s) = \frac{N(s)}{D(s)} = \frac{m_1(s) + n_1(s)}{m_2(s) + n_2(s)} \qquad (1\text{-}9)$$

and define

$$\phi(s) = \tanh^{-1} \frac{n_1(s)}{m_1(s)} - \tanh^{-1} \frac{n_2(s)}{m_2(s)} \quad (1\text{-}10)$$

$$= \tanh^{-1} \frac{n_1 m_2 - n_2 m_1}{m_1 m_2 - n_1 n_2} \quad (1\text{-}11)$$

where the m's and n's are the even and odd parts, respectively, of $N(s)$ and $D(s)$. Then, for $s = j\omega$, we may show

$$\phi(j\omega) = j \tan^{-1} \frac{\text{Im } T(j\omega)}{\text{Re } T(j\omega)} \quad (1\text{-}12)$$

$$= j \tan^{-1} A(\omega) \quad (1\text{-}13)$$

$$= j \arg T(j\omega) \quad (1\text{-}14)$$

where $A(\omega)$ will be termed the angle function. Thus, $A(\omega)$ is a ratio of odd to even polynomials in $\omega$.[†]

To form $T(s)$ from $A(\omega)$, we note

$$j A(\omega) = \frac{n_1 m_2 - n_2 m_1}{m_1 m_2 - n_1 n_2} \bigg|_{s = j\omega} \quad (1\text{-}15)$$

so that

$$[1 + j A(\omega)] \bigg|_{\omega = \frac{s}{j}} = \frac{m_1 m_2 - n_1 n_2 + n_1 m_2 - n_2 m_1}{m_1 m_2 - n_1 n_2} \quad (1\text{-}16)$$

$$= \frac{(m_1 + n_1)(m_2 - n_2)}{m_1 m_2 - n_1 n_2} \quad (1\text{-}17)$$

Thus, given an $A(\omega)$,

$$A(\omega) = \frac{p(\omega)}{q(\omega)} \quad (1\text{-}18)$$

we form $q(\omega) + jp(\omega)$ and substitute $s/j$ for $\omega$. The zeros of the resulting polynomial in s then become zeros or poles of $T(s)$, according to Eq. 1-17, the arbitrariness being similar to that for a magnitude function.

---

† A ratio of even to odd polynomials is also permitted if we remember that an $\omega$ has been canceled in $A(\omega)$. The canceled $\omega$ then yields a zero or pole of $T(s)$ at the origin.

*Example 1.2:*

$$A(\omega) = \frac{-\omega^3 - \omega}{15 - \omega^2} \qquad (1\text{-}19)$$

$$q(\omega) + jp(\omega) = -j\omega^3 - \omega^2 - j\omega + 15 \qquad (1\text{-}20)$$

$$q(\omega) + jp(\omega) \bigg|_{\omega = \frac{s}{j}} = s^3 + s^2 - s + 15 \qquad (1\text{-}21)$$

$$= (s + 3)(s^2 - 2s + 5) \qquad (1\text{-}22)$$

Thus, we may choose

$$T(s) = \frac{s + 3}{s^2 + 2s + 5}, \ (s + 3)(s - 2s + 5), \frac{s - 2s + 5}{s - 3}, \ \dots \qquad (1\text{-}23)$$

In summary, the necessary and sufficient condition that $A(\omega)$ be an angle function is that it be an odd rational function of $\omega$.

*Delay Function.*† Given a transfer function $T(s)$

$$T(s) = \frac{\overset{m}{\pi} (s - z_i)}{\underset{n}{\pi} (s - p_r)} \qquad (1\text{-}24)$$

we form

$$\frac{T(s)}{T(-s)} = (-1)^{m-n} \frac{\overset{m}{\pi}(s - z_i)\overset{n}{\pi}(s + p_r)}{\underset{n}{\pi}(s - p_r)\underset{m}{\pi}(s + z_i)} \qquad (1\text{-}25)$$

It follows that

$$\left| \frac{T(j\omega)}{T(-j\omega)} \right| = 1 \qquad (1\text{-}26)$$

and

$$\ln \frac{T(j\omega)}{T(-j\omega)} = j \arg \frac{T(j\omega)}{T(-j\omega)} \qquad (1\text{-}27)$$

$$= 2j \arg T(j\omega) \qquad (1\text{-}28)$$

---

† See [B2.423] in the bibliography.

We now define the (group) delay

$$D_f(\omega) = -\frac{d}{d\omega} \arg T(j\omega) \qquad (1\text{-}29)$$

and find from Eqs. 1-12 and 1-29

$$D_f(\omega) = \frac{j}{2} \frac{d}{d\omega} \ln \left[ (-1)^{m-n} \frac{\overset{m}{\pi}(j\omega - z_i) \overset{n}{\pi}(j\omega + p_r)}{\overset{n}{\pi}(j\omega - p_r) \overset{m}{\pi}(j\omega + z_i)} \right] \qquad (1\text{-}30)$$

$$= \frac{j}{2} \left[ \sum_i^m \frac{d}{d\omega} \ln \frac{j\omega - z_i}{j\omega + z_i} - \sum_r^n \frac{d}{d\omega} \ln \frac{j\omega - p_r}{j\omega + p_r} \right] \qquad (1\text{-}31)$$

$$= \frac{j}{2} \left[ \sum_i^m \frac{-2j\, z_i}{\omega^2 + z_i^2} - \sum_r^n \frac{-2j\, p_r}{\omega^2 + p_r^2} \right] \qquad (1\text{-}32)$$

$$= \sum_i^m \frac{z_i}{\omega^2 + z_i^2} - \sum_r^n \frac{p_r}{\omega^2 + p_r^2} \qquad (1\text{-}33)$$

Therefore, a necessary condition that a ratio of even polynomials in $\omega$ to be a delay function is that it be expandable into partial fractions in $\omega^2$ with residues as given by Eq. 1-33. To show this is also sufficient, Eq. 1-33 is rewritten

$$-D_f(\omega) = \sum_i^m \frac{-\dfrac{1}{z_i}}{1 + \left(\dfrac{\omega}{z_i}\right)^2} - \sum_r^n \frac{-\dfrac{1}{p_r}}{1 + \left(\dfrac{\omega}{p_r}\right)^2} \qquad (1\text{-}34)$$

Integrating to obtain $\arg T(j\omega)$, we obtain

$$\arg T(j\omega) = \sum_i^m \tan^{-1} \frac{\omega}{-z_i} - \sum_r^n \tan^{-1} \frac{\omega}{-p_r} \qquad (1\text{-}35)$$

which, for $p_r$ and $z_i$ real, we associate with the transfer function

$$T(s) = \frac{\pi(s - z_i)}{\pi(s - p_r)} \qquad (1\text{-}36)$$

A complex pair $p_r$ or $z_i$ in the expansion of $D_f(\omega)$ integrates to terms of the form

$$\tan^{-1} \frac{\omega}{\text{Re } p_r + j \text{ Im } p_r} + \tan^{-1} \frac{\omega}{\text{Re } p_r - j \text{ Im } p_r}$$

$$= \tan^{-1} \frac{2 \text{ Re } p_r \, \omega}{(\text{Re } p_r)^2 + (\text{Im } p_r)^2 - \omega^2} \qquad (1\text{-}37)$$

Eq. 1-37 is evidently the phase contribution of the quadratic factor $s^2 + 2 \text{ Re } p_r + (\text{Re } p_r)^2 + (\text{Im } p_r)^2$. Thus, from any $D_f(\omega)$ with the proper residues, $T(s)$ can be constructed, showing sufficiency.

*Example 1.3:*

$$D_f(\omega) = \frac{\omega^4 + 6\omega^2}{\omega^6 + \omega^4 + 4\omega^2 + 4} \qquad (1\text{-}38)$$

$$= \frac{-1}{\omega^2 + 1} + \frac{1 + j1}{\omega^2 + j2} + \frac{1 - j1}{\omega^2 - j2} \qquad (1\text{-}39)$$

Thus, we can choose†

$$z_1 = -1 \quad p_1 = -1 + j1 \quad p_1{}^* = -1 - j1 \qquad (1\text{-}40)$$

and

$$T(s) = \frac{s + 1}{s^2 + 2s + 2} \qquad (1\text{-}41)$$

## 1.2. Realizability of Ideal Responses

The ideal low-pass filter response will be defined as having the form of Fig. 1-2. The response of the network to a pulse of width $\tau$ may then be calculated to be (Fig. 1-3)

$$g(t) = \frac{1}{\pi} S_i [\omega_c(t - T + \tau/2)] - S_i [\omega_c(t - T - \tau/2)]$$

$$(1\text{-}42)$$

---

† What arbitrariness do we have in choosing the $z_i$ and $p_r$?

(where $S_i(t) = \displaystyle\int_0^t \frac{\sin x}{x}\,dx$) which is not zero for $t < 0$. Therefore,

an output has occurred before an input is applied, clearly an impossibility. Hence, such a characteristic is theoretically unrealizable. A question immediately comes to mind—"Could the ideal magnitude response be obtained if we could accept something besides a linear phase?"

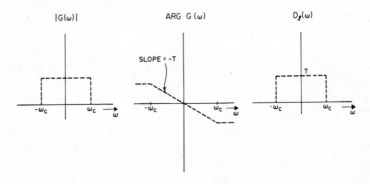

**Fig. 1-2.** An ideal low-pass response.

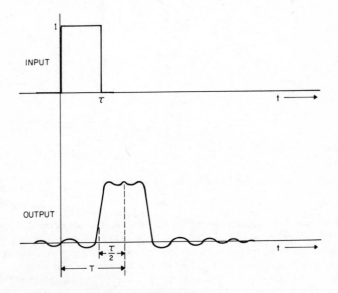

**Fig. 1-3.** Pulse response of an ideal low-pass filter.

*The Paley-Wiener Criterion.* In answering the above question, we employ the Paley-Wiener criterion [B1.102, 1.202, 1.204, 2.106].† According to this theorem a necessary and sufficient condition for an even magnitude function $|G(\omega)|$† to be theoretically realizable is

$$\int_{-\infty}^{\infty} \frac{\left| \log |G(\omega)| \right|}{1 + \omega^2} \, d\omega < \infty \qquad (1\text{-}43)$$

If the integral *is* bounded, then a phase function can be found such that the combined frequency function $|G(\omega)| \; e^{j \arg G(\omega)}$ yields zero transient response for $t < 0$.‡

Note that the above is not intended as a sufficient condition for a physical realization of the network itself; it is, of course, a necessary condition.

If we apply the above criterion to the ideal magnitude characteristic, it is obvious that the integrand is infinite in the stopband and therefore the characteristic is unrealizable. On the other hand, if the stopband specification is non-zero (Fig. 1-4), the characteristic is realizable (it yields zero transient response for $t < 0$).

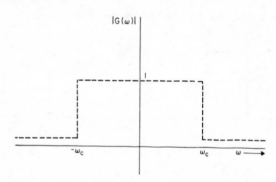

**Fig. 1-4.** Modified ideal magnitude response.

---

† References such as this indicate reference numbers for titles in the bibliography that treat subject matter related to the section in which the reference appears.

† $G(\omega)$ will be used to denote any complex-valued function of $\omega$, either rational or irrational; in contrast, $T(j\omega)$ will be used to represent rational functions.

‡ Specifically, the inverse transform of $[I(\omega) \; e^{j\phi(\omega)}] \; [|G(\omega)| \; e^{j \arg G(\omega)}]$ is zero for $t < 0$, where the former is the Fourier Transform of any $f(t)$ which is zero for $t < 0$.

Given a theoretically realizable $|G(\omega)|$, then, we are interested in finding the corresponding phase function. Unfortunately, the associated arg $G(\omega)$ is not unique.

This arbitrariness in the phase correlates with the fact that for a given rational $|T(j\omega)|^2$ composed of factors of the form $\omega^4 + a_2\omega^2 + a_0$, the poles and zeros of $T(s)$ may be chosen in any combination either in the right or left half-plane as previously noted. If we are given a $|T(j\omega)|^2$, any of a number of different $T(s)$'s and, hence, different arg $T(j\omega)$'s are possible. If, however, we insist upon stable, minimum phase functions (i.e., all poles and zeros of $T(s)$ in the left half-plane), then arg $T(j\omega)$ would be unique. It happens that a similar statement applies to any $G(\omega)$. To obtain this unique phase characteristic in the general case, we employ the Hilbert Transform.

*The Hilbert Transform.* The Hilbert Transform [B1.102] relates the $j\omega$-axis behavior of the real and imaginary parts of a function analytic in the right half-plane and on the $j\omega$-axis.

We note that ln $G(s/j)$ is such a function if $G(s/j)$ is analytic and non-zero in the right half-plane of $j\omega$-axis (i.e., $T(s)$ is stable and minimum phase). Then the Hilbert Transform relates $\ln|G(\omega)| = \alpha(\omega)$, the attenuation, and arg $G(\omega) = \beta(\omega)$, the phase angle:

$$\alpha(\omega) = \frac{1}{\pi} \int_{-\infty}^{\infty} \frac{\beta(\zeta)\ d\zeta}{\omega - \zeta} \tag{1-44}$$

$$\beta(\omega) = -\frac{1}{\pi} \int_{-\infty}^{\infty} \frac{\alpha(\zeta)\ d\zeta}{\omega - \zeta} \tag{1-45}$$

Even when $\alpha(\omega)$ and/or $\beta(\omega)$ is non-analytic at a discrete number of points on the $j\omega$-axis, we can take Eqs. 1-44 and 1-45 as limiting cases of the equations

$$\alpha(\omega) = \frac{1}{\pi} \lim_{\sigma \to 0} \int_{-\infty}^{\infty} \frac{(\omega - \zeta)\ \beta(\zeta)\ d\zeta}{\sigma^2 + (\omega - \zeta)^2} \tag{1-46}$$

$$\beta(\omega) = -\frac{1}{\pi} \lim_{\sigma \to 0} \int_{-\infty}^{\infty} \frac{(\omega - \zeta)\ \alpha(\zeta)\ d\zeta}{\sigma^2 + (\omega - \zeta)^2} \tag{1-47}$$

We are now in a position to evaluate the unique phase function corresponding to the modified ideal approximation (Fig. 1-4). Thus,

$$\beta(\omega) = -\frac{1}{\pi}\lim_{\sigma \to 0}\int_{-\infty}^{-\omega_c}\frac{-\alpha_0\,(\omega - \zeta)\,d\zeta}{\sigma^2 + (\omega - \zeta)^2}$$
$$-\frac{1}{\pi}\lim_{\sigma \to 0}\int_{\omega_c}^{\infty}\frac{-\alpha_0\,(\omega - \zeta)\,d\zeta}{\sigma^2 + (\omega - \zeta)^2} \tag{1-48}$$

$$= -\frac{\alpha_0}{\pi}\lim_{\sigma \to 0}\int_{\omega_c}^{\infty}\left[\frac{-(\omega + \zeta)}{\sigma^2 + (\omega + \zeta)^2}\right.$$
$$\left.-\frac{(\omega - \zeta)}{\sigma^2 + (\omega - \zeta)^2}\right]d\zeta \tag{1-49}$$

$$= +\frac{\alpha_0}{\pi}\lim_{\sigma \to 0}\ln\frac{\sqrt{\sigma^2 + (\omega - \omega_c)^2}}{\sqrt{\sigma^2 + (\omega + \omega_c)^2}} \tag{1-50}$$

$$= \frac{\alpha_0}{\pi}\lim_{\sigma \to 0}\ln\left|\frac{\sigma \pm j(\omega - \omega_c)}{\sigma \pm j(\omega + \omega_c)}\right| = \frac{\alpha_0}{\pi}\ln\left|\frac{\omega - \omega_c}{\omega + \omega_c}\right| \tag{1-51}$$

which has the characteristic of Fig. 1-5. Note that $\beta(\omega)$ is not analytic on the $\omega$-axis, having branch points at $\omega = \pm\,\omega_c$; hence, the limit operation was required in this case, although $\alpha(\omega)$ was itself analytic.

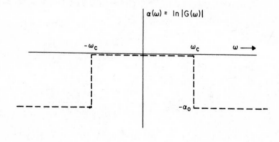

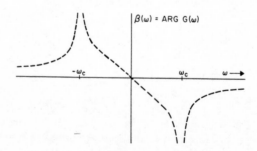

**Fig. 1-5.** Modified ideal magnitude, associated phase response.

It is left as an exercise for the reader to find the delay of this response (assuming that differentiation before taking the limit is permissible).

In summary, we can conclude that

1. The ideal low-pass magnitude characteristic is theoretically unrealizable because of the stopband requirement.

2. A close approximation to the ideal $\alpha(\omega)$ and $\beta(\omega)$ cannot be obtained simultaneously by minimum-phase stable functions, since, as the ideal of either one is approached, the form of the other approaches that shown in Figs. 1-5 or 1-6 (Problem 1.5).

## 1.3. Approximation with Non-Minimum Phase Functions

Although we avoid unstable systems to achieve simultaneous ideal low-pass magnitude and delay, if we are willing to use balanced RLC networks or active networks then non-minimum phase functions have definite approximation advantages.† There are two rather obvious ways of generating such functions [B2.412]:

1. (a) Obtain a $T_1(s)$ with a good low-pass magnitude characteristic.
   (b) Correct the delay characteristic of $T_1(s)$ with a $T_2(s)$ of the all-pass form

$$T_2(s) = \frac{\pi(s^2 - 2\rho_i\omega_i \, s + \omega_i^2)}{\pi(s^2 + 2\rho_i\omega_i \, s + \omega_i^2)} \qquad (1\text{-}52)$$

so that

$$|T(j\omega)| = |T_1(j\omega)| \; |T_2(j\omega)| \qquad (1\text{-}53)$$

$$= |T_1(j\omega)| \qquad (1\text{-}54)$$

This method is discussed further in Chapter 5.

2. (a) Obtain an all-pole function $T_1(s) = 1/D(s)$ which has the desired delay characteristic but reduced by a scale factor of 2.
   (b) Form

$$T_2(s) = \frac{N(s)}{D(s)} \qquad (1\text{-}55)$$

---

† When the poles and zeros of $T(s)$ are located near the imaginary axis (as in the bandpass case) then grounded RLC realizations are possible even though the function is non-minimum phase.

where $N(s)$ is chosen so that $|T_2(j\omega)|$ is the square root of the desired magnitude characteristic.

(c) The desired $T(s)$ is then

$$T(s) = \frac{N(s)N(-s)}{D^2(s)} \qquad (1\text{-}56)$$

It is left as an exercise to show that $T(s)$ is indeed the wanted function. Note that in each of the above methods, desired magnitude and phase specifications may be approximated independently. This implies that the ideal low-pass magnitude and phase characteristics may be approximated arbitrarily closely, once non-minimum phase functions are allowed.

## PROBLEMS

1.1. Which of the following are bona-fide magnitude functions? Defend by finding the functions.

(a) $\dfrac{1}{1 + \omega^2}$

(b) $\dfrac{1}{1 + \dfrac{\omega^2}{\omega^2 - 1}}$

(c) $\dfrac{1}{1 + \left(\dfrac{\omega^2}{\omega^2 - 1}\right)^2}$

(d) $1 + \omega^4$

1.2. Which of the following are angle functions? Find all the associated $T(s)$'s.

(a) $\dfrac{\omega}{1 + \omega^2}$

(b) $\dfrac{\omega}{1 - \omega^2}$

(c) $\omega(1 + \omega^2)$

(d) $\dfrac{1 + \omega^2}{3\omega}$

1.3. What are the necessary and sufficient conditions that an angle function $(A(\omega))$ be that of an all-pole stable transfer function?

1.4. For what values of $K$ is the following a delay function? Find all the possible $T(s)$'s.

$$D_\ell(\omega) = K \frac{\omega^2 - 3}{(\omega^2 + 1)(\omega^2 + 9)}$$

**1.5.** Show that the ideal phase characteristic of Fig. 1-6a has an associate $\alpha(\omega)$ of the form of Fig. 1-6b.

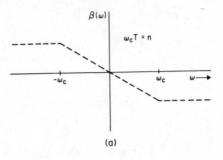

(a)

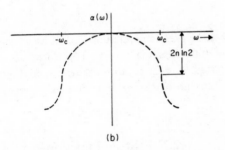

(b)

**Fig. 1-6.** Ideal phase, associated magnitude response.

**1.6.** It is claimed that the difference in the degrees of the numerator and denominator polynomials of a delay function must be two. Defend or refute.

# 2

# EQUI-RIPPLE FUNCTIONS

The study of more precise approximation theory presupposes a cursory knowledge of elliptic function theory. Therefore, we must proceed, at present unmotivated, to gain an acquaintance with elliptic functions and a knowledge of the use of elliptic functions in generating rational functions.

## 2.1. Elliptic Functions

*Definitions.* For the purposes of this chapter, the study of elliptic functions will begin by defining the integral

$$z(\phi;m) = \int_0^\phi \frac{d\,\Omega}{\sqrt{(1 - m\,\sin^2\Omega)}} \qquad (2\text{-}1)$$

which is known as an elliptic integral of the first kind. Unfortunately, z may not be integrated directly, although series expansions do allow the computation of z for a given $\phi$ and m† (known as the parameter).

If Eq. 2-1 is interpreted as a transformation from the $\phi$ to the z variable (with m constant), the following functions (known as the Jacobian elliptic functions) may be defined:

---

† Some authors prefer to use k or $\theta$ as a parameter; m may be calculated from either: $m=k^2 = \sin^2\theta$. Alho $0 \leqslant m \leqslant 1$ for our purposes, although this is, in general, not required.

14

$$\text{sn } z = \sin \phi \qquad \text{(elliptic sine)} \qquad (2\text{-}2)$$

$$\text{cn } z = \cos \phi \qquad \text{(elliptic cosine)} \qquad (2\text{-}3)$$

In a manner analogous to that involving circular functions, the following are then defined:

$$\text{sc } z = \frac{\text{sn } z}{\text{cn } z} \qquad \text{(elliptic tangent)} \qquad (2\text{-}4)$$

$$\text{cs } z = \frac{\text{cn } z}{\text{sn } z} \qquad \text{(elliptic cotangent)} \qquad (2\text{-}5)$$

$$\text{nc } z = \frac{1}{\text{cn } z} \qquad \text{(elliptic secant)} \qquad (2\text{-}6)$$

$$\text{ns } z = \frac{1}{\text{sn } z} \qquad \text{(elliptic cosecant)} \qquad (2\text{-}7)$$

Unlike circular function theory, it is also convenient to define an additional function,

$$\text{dn } z = (1 - m \text{ sn}^2 z)^{1/2} \qquad (2\text{-}8)$$

from which the following are defined:

$$\text{nd } z = \frac{1}{\text{dn } z} \qquad (2\text{-}9)$$

$$\text{ds } z = \frac{\text{dn } z}{\text{sn } z} \qquad (2\text{-}10)$$

$$\text{sd } z = \frac{\text{sn } z}{\text{dn } z} \qquad (2\text{-}11)$$

$$\text{dc } z = \frac{\text{dn } z}{\text{cn } z} \qquad (2\text{-}12)$$

$$\text{cd } z = \frac{\text{cn } z}{\text{dn } z} \qquad (2\text{-}13)$$

Thus, there are a total of 12 elliptic functions of interest. If it is desirable to call special attention to the parameter m, the above may be written as sn $(z;m)$.

From Eq. 2-1, we see that

$$z \ (-\phi;m) = -z(\phi;m) \qquad (2\text{-}14)$$

so that

$$\text{sn } [-z(\phi;m)] = \text{sn } [z(-\phi;m)] \qquad (2\text{-}15)$$

$$= \sin [-\phi] \qquad (2\text{-}16)$$

$$= -\sin \phi \qquad (2\text{-}17)$$

$$= -\text{sn } [z(\phi;m)] \qquad (2\text{-}18)$$

Similarly, we may show that

$$\text{cn } (-z) = \text{cn } z \qquad (2\text{-}19)$$

$$\text{dn } (-z) = \text{dn } z \qquad (2\text{-}20)$$

**Degenerate Elliptic Functions.** If $m = 0$ in Eq. 2-1, $z = \phi$ and, from Eqs. 2-2 - 2-13, the elliptic functions degenerate to the circular functions.

$$\text{sn } (z;0) = \sin z \qquad (2\text{-}21)$$

$$\text{cn } (z;0) = \cos z \qquad (2\text{-}22)$$

$$\text{dn } (z;0) = 1 \qquad (2\text{-}23)$$

etc.

When $m = 1$, Eq. 2-1 becomes

$$z = \int_0^\phi \frac{d\Omega}{\cos \Omega} \qquad (2\text{-}24)$$

$$= \text{sech}^{-1} \cos \phi = \tanh^{-1} \sin \phi \qquad (2\text{-}25)$$

so that

$$\text{sn } (z;1) = \sin \phi \qquad \text{(from Eq. 2-2)} \qquad (2\text{-}26)$$

$$= \tanh z \qquad \text{(from Eq. 2-25)} \qquad (2\text{-}27)$$

Similarly, we can show

$$\text{cn } (z;1) = \text{dn } (z;1) = \cos \phi \qquad (2\text{-}28)$$

$$= \text{sech } z \qquad (2\text{-}29)$$

Thus, both circular and hyperbolic functions are special cases of elliptic functions.

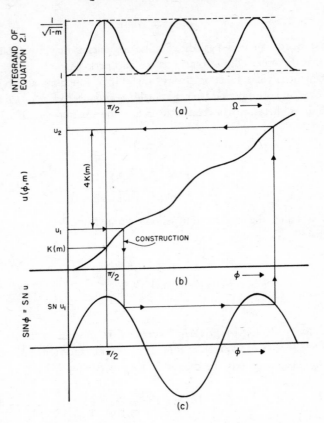

**Fig. 2-1.** Construction showing periodicity of sn.

*Real Period of Elliptic Functions.* In Fig. 2-1 the integrand of Eq. 2-1 is plotted.[†] If u† $(\phi;m)$ is interpreted as the area under the curve, u may then be plotted as a function of $\phi$ (Fig. 2-1a). But $\sin \phi = $ sn u, so that for any given value of u ($u_1$ in Fig. 2-1b), sn $u_1$ (Fig. 2-1c) may be found by the simple construction shown.

Since $\sin \phi$ is periodic, we may easily find other values of u ($u_n$) such that sn $u_1 = $ sn $u_n$. The construction for finding $u_2$ is shown. Because of the symmetry of u $(\phi;m)$ and the periodicity of $\sin \phi$, however, it is clear that

---

† For $\phi$, $\Omega$ real.

† $z = u + jv$.

$$u_n - u_{n-1} = \text{constant} \qquad (2\text{-}30)$$

In other words, sn u is periodic. Similar arguments may be applied to show that the other elliptic functions are also periodic.

Just as in circular function theory, any elliptic function can be reproduced over an entire period from a knowledge of its behavior in a quarter-period. It is therefore convenient to define the quarter-period

$$K\ (m) \equiv u \left( \frac{\pi}{2}; m \right) \qquad (2\text{-}31)$$

$$= \int_0^{\pi/2} \frac{d\Omega}{\sqrt{1 - m\ \sin^2 \Omega}} \qquad (2\text{-}32)$$

$K(m)$ is called the *real* quarter-period.[†] From Figs. 2-1a and 2-1b we immediately calculate

$$\text{sn}\ [K(m); m] = 1 \qquad (2\text{-}33)$$

$$\text{sn}\ [2K(m); m] = 0 \qquad (2\text{-}34)$$

etc.

*Imaginary Period of Elliptic Functions.* In contrast to circular functions (but similar to hyperbolic functions) elliptic functions are periodic along the imaginary axis. To show this, we re-write Eq. 2-1

$$z = \int_0^\phi \frac{d\Omega}{\sqrt{1 - m\ \sin^2 \Omega}} \qquad (2\text{-}35)$$

and make the change in variable

$$\sin \Omega = j \tan \zeta \qquad (2\text{-}36)$$

so that

$$\cos \Omega = \sqrt{1 - \sin^2 \Omega} \qquad (2\text{-}37)$$

$$= \sqrt{1 + \tan^2 \zeta} \qquad (2\text{-}38)$$

$$= \sec \zeta \qquad (2\text{-}39)$$

Then, we have

$$\sqrt{1 - m\ \sin^2 \Omega} = \sqrt{1 + m\ \tan^2 \zeta} \qquad (2\text{-}40)$$

[†] Note $K(0) = \dfrac{\pi}{2}$, $K(1) = \infty$.

$$= \sec \zeta \sqrt{1 - (1 - m) \sin^2 \zeta} \qquad (2\text{-}41)$$

We may now define a complementary parameter

$$m_1 = 1 - m \qquad (2\text{-}42)$$

so that Eq. 2-40 becomes

$$\sqrt{1 - m \sin^2 \Omega} = \sec \zeta \sqrt{1 - m_1 \sin^2 \zeta} \qquad (2\text{-}43)$$

Also, we have

$$d(\sin \Omega) = j \ d(\tan \zeta) \qquad (2\text{-}44)$$

$$\cos \Omega \ d\Omega = j \sec^2 \zeta \ d\zeta \qquad (2\text{-}45)$$

and

$$d\Omega = j \sec \zeta \ d\zeta \qquad (2\text{-}46)$$

using Eq. 2-39. Substitution of Eqs. 2-43 and 2-46 into Eq. 2-35 yields

$$-jz = \int_0^\gamma \frac{d\zeta}{\sqrt{1 - m_1 \sin^2 \zeta}} \qquad (2\text{-}47)$$

where

$$\gamma = \tan^{-1} (-j \sin \phi) \quad \text{(from Eq. 2-36)} \qquad (2\text{-}48)$$

Since Eq. 2-47 is of the same form as Eq. 2-35, we have, from the definition of the elliptic functions (Eqs. 2-2 - 2-13),

$$\text{sn} \ (-jz;m_1) = \sin \gamma \qquad \text{cn} \ (-jz;m_1) = \cos \gamma \qquad (2\text{-}49)$$

whereas

$$\text{sn} \ (z;m) = \sin \phi \qquad (2\text{-}50)$$

$$= j \ \frac{\sin \gamma}{\cos \gamma} \quad \text{(from Eq. 2-48)} \qquad (2\text{-}51)$$

$$= j \ \frac{\text{sn} \ (-jz;m_1)}{\text{cn} \ (-jz;m_1)} \quad \text{(from Eq. 2-49)} \qquad (2\text{-}52)$$

$$= j \ \text{sc} \ (-jz;m_1) \qquad (2\text{-}53)$$

We finally conclude

$$\text{sn} \ (jz;m) = j \ \text{sc} \ (z;m_1) \qquad (2\text{-}54)$$

Now sc $(z;m_1)$ has a real quarter-period $K(m_1) = K(1 - m)$ so that, from Eq. 2-54, sn $(z;m)$ has an imaginary quarter-period $K(m_1)$ in addition to its real quarter-period of $K(m)$. It may likewise be shown that

$$\text{cn } (jz;m) = \frac{1}{\text{cn } (z;m_1)} \qquad (2\text{-}55)$$

$$\text{dn } (jz;m) = \frac{\text{dn } (z;m_1)}{\text{cn } (z;m_1)} \qquad (2\text{-}56)$$

$$\text{sc } (jz;m) = j \text{ sn } (z;m_1) \qquad (2\text{-}57)$$

For example, we have

$$\text{cn } [j \text{ } K(m_1);m] = \frac{1}{\text{cn } [K(m_1);m_1]} \qquad (2\text{-}58)$$

$$= \frac{1}{\cos \pi/2} \text{ (from Eq. 2-3)} \quad (2\text{-}59)$$

$$= \infty \qquad (2\text{-}60)$$

Unlike the circular and hyperbolic functions, then, elliptic functions may have finite poles.

*Behavior in the Complex Plane.* Knowing the behavior of sn $z$, cn $z$, etc., on the real and imaginary axis, we can evaluate them anywhere in the complex plane by means of well-known addition formulae (Table 2.5, p. 46) similar to those involving circular functions. Table 2.1 (p. 44) gives the values of important elliptic functions for various values of $z$ on the rectangle bounded in the z-plane by the real and imaginary quarter-periods $K(m)$ and $K(m_1)$, respectively. In addition, the pole-zero distribution of these functions is shown in Fig. 2-9 (p. 30) over a portion of the z-plane about the origin. By means of the periodicity requirement, one may evidently extend the tables and figures to include positions throughout the z-plane.

*Elliptic Formulae.* It is possible to relate the parameter $m$ (and, hence, $m_1$) to the quarter-periods, since the latter are defined in terms of the former (Eq. 2-31). These relationships are given below together with formulae necessary to evaluate the Jacobian elliptic functions anywhere on the real (or imaginary) axis. Of course, tables of elliptic functions [B2.112, 2.114] are also available for calculation of sn $z$, cn $z$, dn $z$, and $K(m)$.

The following formulae are given in [B2.112]:

Define

$$\ell = \frac{1}{2} \times \frac{(1 - m_1^{1/4})}{(1 + m_1^{1/4})} \tag{2-61}$$

$$q = \ell + 2\ell^5 + 15\ell^9 + 150\ell^{13} + \dots \tag{2-62}$$

Then

$$\frac{K(m_1)}{K(m)} = \frac{1}{\pi} \ln 1/q$$

$$K(m) = \frac{\pi}{2} (1 + 2q + 2q^4 + 2q^9 + \dots)^2 \tag{2-63}$$

The reader may show that, for m near 0,†

$$\frac{K(m_1)}{K(m)} \approx \frac{1}{\pi} \ln \frac{16}{m} \tag{2-64}$$

or, for m near 1,

$$\frac{K(m)}{K(m_1)} \approx \frac{1}{\pi} \ln \frac{16}{m_1} \tag{2-65}$$

Also,

$$\text{sn } (u;m) = \left( \frac{1 + 2q + 2q^4 + 2q^9 + \dots}{1 + q^2 + q^6 + q^{12} + \dots} \right)$$
$$\times \left( \frac{\sin \pi u' - q^2 \sin 3\pi u' + q^6 \sin 5\pi u' - \dots}{D(q;u')} \right) \tag{2-66}$$

$$\text{cn } (u;m) = \left( \frac{1 - 2q + 2q^4 - 2q^9 + \dots}{1 + q^2 + q^6 + q^{12} + \dots} \right)$$
$$\times \left( \frac{\cos \pi u' + q^2 \cos 3\pi u' + q^6 \cos 5\pi u' + \dots}{D(q;u')} \right) . \tag{2-67}$$

---

† For m near 1, interchange m and $m_1$ and define $\ell_1$, $q_1$, etc. Then it may be shown that in $\ln q \ln q_1 = \pi^2$.

$$dn\ (u;m) = \left(\frac{1 - 2q + 2q^4 - 2q^9 + \ldots}{1 + 2q + 2q^4 + 2q^9 + \ldots}\right)$$

$$\times \left(\frac{1 + 2q \cos 2\pi u' + 2q^4 \cos 4\pi u' + 2q^9 \cos 6\pi u' + \ldots}{D(q;u')}\right)$$

$$(2\text{-}68)$$

where

$$D(q;u') = 1 - 2q \cos 2\pi u' + 2q^4 \cos 4\pi u' - 2q^9 \cos 6\pi u' + \ldots$$

$$(2\text{-}69)$$

$$u' = \frac{u}{2K(m)} \qquad (2\text{-}70)$$

*Example 2.1:* Find

$$z_1 = sn\left[\frac{2K(m)}{3} - j.438; .566\right] \qquad (2\text{-}71)$$

We calculate from formulae (or a table) $K(m) = 1.909$. Then, from Tables 2.2 and 2.5 (p. 44 and p. 46)

$$z_1 = [sn\ (1.277;m)\ dn\ (-.438;m_1) \times j\ cn\ (1.277;m)$$
$$\times\ dn\ (1.277;m)\ sn\ (-.438;m_1)\ cn\ (-.438;m_1)]$$
$$\div\ cn^2\ (-.438;m_1) + (.566)\ sn^2\ (1.277;m)\ sn^2\ (-.438;m_1)$$

where $m = .566$, $m_1 = .434$. Finally, evaluating each of the above, we have

$$z_1 = \frac{(.906)(.962) - j(.420)(.730)(.420)(.908)}{(.908)^2 + .566(.906)^2(.420)^2} \qquad (2\text{-}73)$$

$$= .962 - j.129 \qquad (2\text{-}74)$$

## 2.2 Rational Functions Derivable from Circular and Elliptic Functions

*Introduction.* Certain combinations of trigonometric and inverse trigonometric functions are useful in approximation theory because of their extremal properties. Since only rational functions qualify as parts of realizable network functions, we should first familiarize ourselves with the form of such functions and the conditions under which they are rational.

*Circular Derivations.* Let us consider the function

$$C_n(\omega) = \cos n \, \cos^{-1} \omega \qquad (2\text{-}75)$$

where n is a positive integer. Then

$$C_1(\omega) = \cos (\cos^{-1} \omega) \qquad (2\text{-}76)$$

$$= \omega \qquad (2\text{-}77)$$

$$C_2(\omega) = \cos 2 (\cos^{-1} \omega) \qquad (2\text{-}78)$$

$$= 2\omega^2 - 1 \qquad (2\text{-}79)$$

$$C_3(\omega) = \cos 3 (\cos^{-1} \omega) \qquad (2\text{-}80)$$

$$= 4\omega^3 - 3\omega \qquad (2\text{-}81)$$

etc.

On the other hand, if we define

$$S_n(\omega) = \sin n \, \cos^{-1} \omega \qquad (2\text{-}82)$$

then

$$S_1(\omega) = \sin (\cos^{-1} \omega) \qquad (2\text{-}83)$$

$$= \sqrt{1 - \cos^2 (\cos^{-1} \omega)} \qquad (2\text{-}84)$$

$$= \sqrt{1 - \omega^2} \qquad (2\text{-}85)$$

$$S_2(\omega) = 2\omega \sqrt{1 - \omega^2} \qquad (2\text{-}86)$$

$$S_3(\omega) = \sqrt{1 - \omega^2} (4\omega^2 - 1) \qquad (2\text{-}87)$$

It is of interest to find out why $C_n(\omega)$ is apparently always a polynomial, whereas $S_n(\omega)$ is not.

To begin, we define the variable

$$z = \cos^{-1} \omega \qquad (2\text{-}88)$$

and we then construct the path followed in the z-plane as $\omega$ varies from $-\infty$ to $+\infty$ in the s-plane (Fig. 2-2). This is facilitated by writing

$$z = - \int \frac{d\omega}{1 - \omega^2} \qquad (2\text{-}89)$$

$$= j \int \frac{ds}{s^2 + 1} \qquad (2\text{-}90)$$

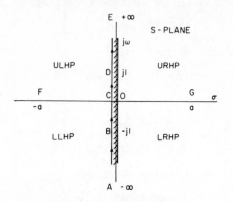

**Fig. 2-2. S-plane definition of path.**

(by analytic continuation) and interpreting Eq. 2-90 as an example of the Schwartz-Christoffel transformation ·

$$z = A \int \pi(s - s_i)^{-a_i} ds + B \qquad (2\text{-}91)$$

where $s_1 = j1$, $s_2 = -j1$, $a_1 = a_2 = \frac{1}{2}$, $A = j1$, $B = 0$. Therefore, as $\omega$ travels its path, the associated z-plane mapping must undergo an angular change of $+90°$ at $s = \pm j1$. This, together with the conditions

$$\omega = -\infty \qquad\qquad z = -\pi + j\infty \qquad (2\text{-}92)$$

$$\omega = -1 \qquad\qquad z = -\pi \qquad (2\text{-}93)$$

$$\omega = 0 \qquad\qquad z = \pi/2 \qquad (2\text{-}94)$$

$$\omega = +1 \qquad\qquad z = 0 \qquad (2\text{-}95)$$

$$\omega = +\infty \qquad\qquad z = +j\infty \qquad (2\text{-}96)$$

enables us to construct the path in the z-plane (rectangle I in Fig. 2-3a). But, from the condition

$$\omega = \cos z = \cos (-z) \qquad (2\text{-}97)$$

we conclude that rectangle II is also a bona-fide z-plane path. Finally, the periodicity of cos z requires the horizontal symmetry shown in Fig. 2-3a. By assuming an s-plane path from $\sigma = -\infty$ to $\sigma = +\infty$ the reader may, by similar reasoning, obtain the complete z-plane map of the s-plane (Fig. 2-3b).

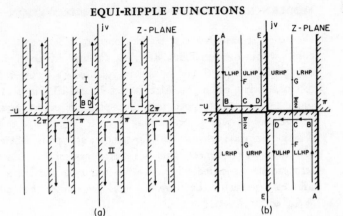

**Fig. 2-3.** Mapping of $z = \cos^{-1} \omega$.

Next, we note that

$$C_n(\omega) = \cos nz \qquad (2\text{-}98)$$

and so we can locate the zeros of $C_n(\omega)$ in the nz-plane where

$$nz = \pm (\pi/2 + 2k\pi) \qquad k = 0, 1, 2, \ldots \qquad (2\text{-}99)$$

Finally, we superimpose the multi-valued z-plane path (as $\omega$ varies) on this nz-plane and note that when n is an integer, the zeros of $C_n(\omega)$ occur at the same $\omega_i$'s within each rectangular path (Fig. 2-4). In contrast, for non-integral n, one of the following can occur:†

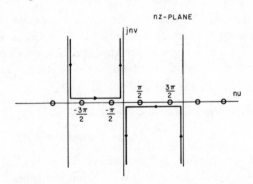

**Fig. 2-4.** NZ-plane mapping of $z = \cos^{-1} \omega$ (n = 2).

† A more rigorous derivation in terms of Riemann surfaces is given by Tuttle [B1.105].

(a) The nz-plane zeros of cos nz may not occur at corresponding points within the rectangles. Referring to Figs. 2-2 and 2-5a, for example, a zero of $C_n(\omega)$ would be required to occur at M in rectangle I but not at M in rectangles II and III. Since M is a single point when mapped into the s-plane, it cannot give rise to a zero of $C_n(\omega)$.

(b) A single nz-plane zero of cos nz may occur at a point where two adjacent rectangles meet. This is a special case of (a), since the zero can be associated with only one rectangle and hence contributes a factor of the form $(\omega + \omega_i)^{1/2}$, rather than a zero, to $C_n(\omega)$.

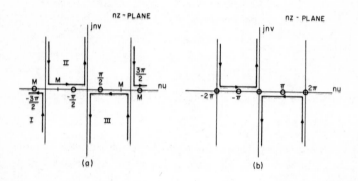

**Fig. 2-5.** Generation of rational functions.

We may now readily show that $\sin n \cos^{-1} \omega$ cannot be polynomial by superimposing the rectangular paths on the nz-plane zero locations of $\sin$ nz (Fig. 2-5b), for we note that two rectangles always meet at $nz = 0$ ($\omega = +1$), which is a zero of $\sin$ nz. Hence, Condition (b) occurs and $S_n(\omega)$ has one factor of the form $\sqrt{1 - \omega}$.

*Elliptic Derivations.* The conditions in which

$$E_n(\omega) = cn\ [n\ cn^{-1}\ (\omega;m);m'] \qquad (2\text{-}100)$$

is a rational function will now be studied. Note that, as $m \to 0$ and $m' \to 0$, $E_n(\omega) \to C_n(\omega)$, so that this section is a generalization of the previous one.

Following the previous procedure, we let

$$z = cn^{-1}\ (\omega;m) \qquad (2\text{-}101)$$

and construct the z-plane mapping of the path of Fig. 2-6. Again, we are aided by the integral (Table 2.3, p. 45)

$$\int \frac{d\omega}{\left\{\left[1 + \left(\frac{\omega}{a}\right)^2\right][1 - \omega^2]\right\}^{1/2}} = \frac{a}{(a^2 + 1)^{1/2}}$$

$$\times cn^{-1}\left[\omega; \frac{1}{(a^2 + 1)}\right] \tag{2-102}$$

which requires the z-plane mapping to bend by $+90°$ at $\omega = \pm 1, \pm ja$.

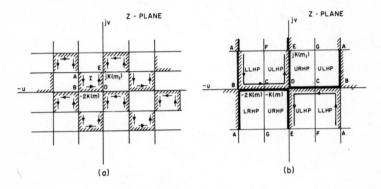

**Fig. 2-6.** Mapping of $z = cn^{-1}\ \omega$.

Also, from Tables 2.1 and 2.5, we can obtain (similar to Eqs. 2-92 - 2-96),

$$cn\ [-2K(m) + jK(m_1); m] = -\infty \tag{2-103}$$

$$cn\ [-2K(m); m] = -1 \tag{2-104}$$

$$cn\ [-K(m); m] = 0 \tag{2-105}$$

$$cn\ (0; m) = +1 \tag{2-106}$$

$$cn\ [+jK(m); m] = +\infty \tag{2-107}$$

These points lie on the sides and corners of rectangle I (Fig. 2-6a). Because cn is an even function, and from the periodicity of cn, we obtain the desired z-plane paths that are shown in Fig. 2-6a. Choosing a path along the $\sigma$-axis in the s-plane, we find the associated z-plane path (EFCGE in Fig. 2-6b). The mapping of the entire s-plane is also shown in Fig. 2-6b.

We can now use the shape of the path of Fig. 2-6 to take a walk through the pole-zero pattern of cn $(nz;m')$. Several such walks are productive in obtaining a rational function.

(a) If $m' = m$

$$E_n(\omega) = cn \, [n \, cn^{-1} \, (\omega;m);m] \qquad (2\text{-}108)$$

and $E_n(\omega)$ is a rational function for all integral n. Thus, we have, from Table 2.5

$$E_2(\omega) = cn \, [2 \, cn^{-1} \, (\omega;m);m] \qquad (2\text{-}109)$$

$$= \frac{cn^2 \, [cn^{-1} \, \omega] \, -sn^2 \, [cn^{-1} \, \omega] \times dn^2 \, [cn^{-1} \, \omega]}{1 \, - \, m \, sn^4 \, [cn^{-1} \, \omega]} \qquad (2\text{-}110)$$

$$= \frac{\omega^2 \, -(1 \, + \, \omega^2)\,(m_1 \, + \, m\omega^2)}{1 \, - \, m \, (1 \, - \, \omega^2)^2} \qquad (2\text{-}111)$$

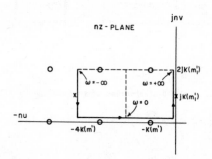

**Fig. 2-7.** Generation of the rational function ($m = m'$).

The walk is shown in Fig. 2-7. How many zeros does $E_2(\omega)$ have on the $\omega$-axis?

(b) If

$$n = \frac{NK(m')}{K(m)} = \frac{K(m_1')}{K(m_1)} \quad N \text{ odd positive integer†}$$

$$(2\text{-}112)$$

---

† We note that if N is even, a zero in the pole-zero configuration of sn (nz) occurs at the point F (Fig. 2-6b), which violates Condition b, but now for the $\sigma$ − axis path EFCGE.

then the path in the nz-plane is shown in Fig. 2-8 for $N = 3$. We may verify this path by noting

$$\omega = 0 \quad z = -K(m) \quad nz = \frac{3K(m')}{K(m)} \times -K(m) = -3K(m') \tag{2-113}$$

$$\omega = \infty \quad z = jK(m_1) \quad nz = \frac{K(m_1')}{K(m_1)} \times jK(m_1) = jK(m_1') \tag{2-114}$$

$$\omega = -\infty \quad z = -2K(m) + jK(m_1) \quad nz = -6K(m') + jK(m_1') \tag{2-115}$$

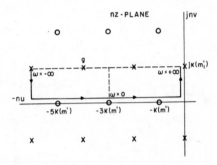

**Fig. 2-8.** Generation of rational function

$$\left[ n = \frac{NK(m')}{K(m)} = \frac{K(m'_1)}{K(m_1)} \right].$$

To transform the pole and zero locations from the nz-plane to the s-plane, we note the following (in the case of the pole at g):

$$nz = -4K(m') + jK(m_1') \tag{2-116}$$

$$z = \frac{-4}{n} K(m') + j \frac{1}{n} [K(m_1')] \tag{2-117}$$

$$= \frac{K(m)}{3K(m')} [-4K(m')] + j \frac{K(m_1)}{K(m_1')} K[(m_1')] \tag{2-118}$$

$$= \frac{-4}{3} K(m) + jK(m_1) \tag{2-119}$$

yielding

$$\omega = cn \left[ -\frac{4}{3} K(m) + jK(m_1); m \right] \tag{2-120}$$

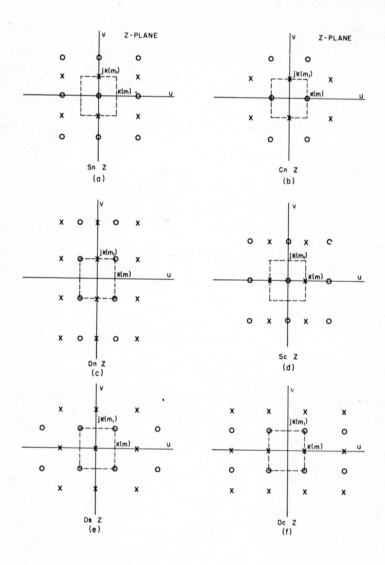

Fig. 2-9. Pole-zero configuration of elliptic functions.

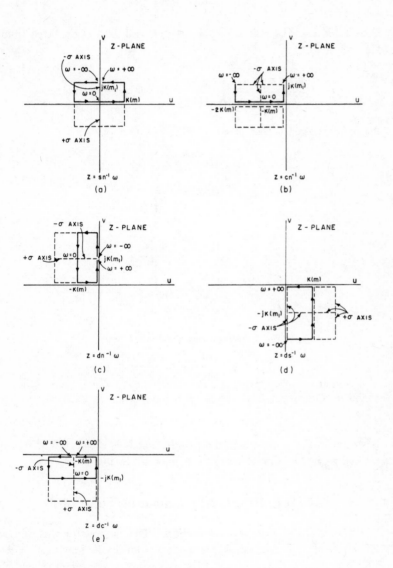

**Fig. 2-10.** Mappings of inverse elliptic functions.

$$= j \ m^{1/2} \ ds \left[ \frac{4}{3} \ K(m); m \right] \tag{2-121}$$

from Table 2.4. The pole is on the negative real axis, as predicted from Fig. 2-8.

(c) If

$$n = \frac{NK(m_1')}{K(m_1)} = \frac{K(m')}{K(m)} \qquad N \text{ odd positive integer}$$

$$\tag{2-122}$$

the path followed is that shown in Fig. 2-11 (for $N = 3$).

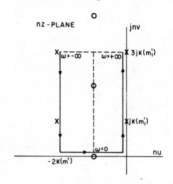

**Fig. 2-11.** Generation of rational function

$$\left[ n = \frac{NK(m_1')}{K(m_1)} = \frac{K(m')}{K(m)} \right].$$

*Other Mappings.* The z-plane path traveled $(-\infty \leqslant \omega \leqslant \infty)$ for

$$z = sn^{-1}(\omega; m) \tag{2-123}$$

is shown in Fig. 2-9a, where the mapped $\sigma$-axis is shown. Mappings of the other inverse elliptic functions of interest are also given.

## 2.3. Equi-Ripple Approximating Functions

*The Case for Equi-Ripple Functions.* The purpose of this section is to provide the motivation for seeking equi-ripple functions as desirable approximating functions. The following is a theorem which, although not proved here, provides this motivation.

Given the interval $[\omega_1, \omega_2]$ on the real $\omega$-axis and the real valued function $f(\omega)$, form the expression

$$F(\omega) = \frac{N(\omega)}{D(\omega)} \qquad (2\text{-}124)$$

$$= \frac{q_0 + q_1\omega + \ldots + q_n\omega^n}{p_0 + p_1\omega + \ldots p_m\omega^m} \qquad (2\text{-}125)$$

where m and n are given. We then propose the problem of determining the $p_i$ and $q_i$ so that

$$\epsilon = \max |f(\omega) - F(\omega)| \text{ for } \omega_1 \leqslant \omega \leqslant \omega_2 \qquad (2\text{-}126)$$

is minimized.

Tchebycheff's Theorem [B2.118]: If the optimizing ratio of polynomials is

$$F(\omega) = \frac{a_0 + a_1\,\omega + \ldots a_{n-v}\,\omega^{n-v}}{b_1 + b_1\,\omega + \ldots b_{m-u}\,\omega^{m-u}}$$
$$\text{for } 0 \leqslant v \leqslant n \text{ and } 0 \leqslant u \leqslant m \qquad (2\text{-}127)$$

then the number N of consecutive points on the interval $[\omega_1,\ \omega_2]$ at which the difference

$$f(\omega) - F(\omega) \qquad (2\text{-}128)$$

with alternate changes in sign takes on the value $\pm\ \epsilon$ is not less than m + n + 1 - d, where d = min (v, u).

In most cases, u = v = d = 0, so that $F(\omega)$ must ripple equally on both sides of $f(\omega)$ a total of at least m + n + 1 times if otherwise unconstrained. The reader is referred to the problems for an application of this theorem.

*Derivation of Equi-Ripple Functions.* It will later be shown that certain desired network responses can be formed from one of the characteristics of Fig. 2-12 where $F(\omega)$ is a ratio of polynomials, both or either of which are even or odd in $\omega$. The generation of these characteristics will be discussed individually.

*Even, Odd Approximation of Zero.* From Fig. 2-12a we require (necessary conditions)

$$(a)\ \frac{d(F)}{d\omega} = 0 \text{ implies } F = +1, \frac{d^2 F}{d^2\,\omega} \leqslant 0 \left.\begin{array}{c} (2\text{-}129) \\[6pt] \\ = -1, \frac{d^2 F}{d^2\,\omega} \geqslant 0 \end{array}\right\} -1 \leqslant \omega \leqslant 1$$
$$(2\text{-}130)$$

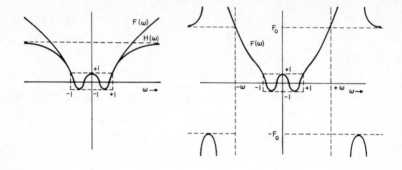

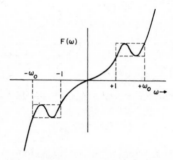

**Fig. 2-12.** (a) Even, odd approximation of zero $(\omega^2 \leq 1)$.
(b) Even, odd approximation of zero $(\omega^2 \leq 1)$ and infinity $(\omega_0^2 \leq \omega^2)$.
(c) Odd approximation constant $(1 \leq \omega^2 \leq \omega_0^2)$.

(b) $\quad F\big|_{\omega = \pm 1} = \pm 1 \qquad\qquad\qquad\qquad\qquad\qquad$ (2-131)

(c) $\quad \dfrac{d(F)}{d\omega} > 0 \quad \begin{array}{l} \text{for } \omega = \pm 1 \quad F \text{ odd} \\ \text{for } \omega = +1 \quad F \text{ even} \end{array} \qquad\qquad$ (2-132)

$\qquad \dfrac{d(F)}{d\omega} < 0 \quad \text{for } \omega = -1 \quad F \text{ even} \qquad\qquad$ (2-133)

Let us consider as an equi-ripple candidate the solution of the differential equation

$$\left(\frac{dF}{d\omega}\right)^2 - k^2 \, \frac{(1 - F^2)}{1 - \omega^2} \, L \, (\omega) = 0 \qquad (2\text{-}134)$$

where $L(\omega)$ has no poles or zeros in the interval $-1 \leq \omega \leq +1$. Note that

$$\frac{dF}{d\omega} = 0 \rightleftharpoons F = \pm 1 \qquad -1 < \omega < +1 \qquad (2\text{-}135)$$

and

$$F(\pm 1) = \pm 1 \qquad (2\text{-}136)$$

(assuming $dF(\pm 1)/d\omega \neq \infty$). Finally, it may be shown that

$$\left.\frac{d^2 F(\omega)}{d\omega^2}\right|_{F = \pm 1} = \frac{(\mp 1)\, L(\omega)}{1 - \omega^2} \qquad (2\text{-}137)$$

thus fulfilling Eqs. 2-129 and 2-130.

The conditions above are not sufficient to obtain a rational equi-ripple $F(\omega)$, their purpose being to associate pictorially the equi-ripple behavior with the following.

Let us assume $L(\omega)$ is of the form

$$L(\omega) = \frac{P^2\,(\omega)}{Q^2\,(\omega)} = \frac{\overset{p}{\pi}(\omega^2 + a_i^2)^2}{\underset{q}{\pi}(\omega^2 + b_i^2)^2} \qquad (2\text{-}138)$$

where P and Q are even functions of $\omega$ where $p \leqslant q$. We can now separate Eq. 2-134

$$-\frac{dF}{\sqrt{1 - F^2}} = -\frac{kPd\omega}{Q\sqrt{1 - \omega^2}} \qquad (2\text{-}139)$$

Integrating, we have

$$\cos^{-1} F = -k \int \frac{\overset{p}{\pi}\,(\omega^2 + a_i^2)}{\underset{q}{\pi}\,(\omega^2 + b_i^2)\,\sqrt{1 - \omega^2}} + c \; a_i, \, b_i, \text{ real or complex} \qquad (2\text{-}140)$$

$$= -k \int \left[ \frac{d_0}{\sqrt{1 - \omega^2}} + \sum_1^q \frac{d_i}{(\omega^2 + b_i^2)\,\sqrt{1 - \omega^2}} \right] d\omega + c \qquad (2\text{-}141)$$

$$= n \, \cos^{-1} \omega - \sum_i^q k_i \, \tan^{-1} \frac{c_i \omega}{\sqrt{1 - \omega^2}} + c \qquad (2\text{-}142)$$

where $n = kd_0$ and

$$\frac{1}{c_i{}^2 - 1} = b_i{}^2 \qquad (2\text{-}143)$$

Solving for $F(\omega)$, we have

$$F(\omega) = \cos\left[ n \cos^{-1} \omega - \sum_{i}^{q} k_i \tan^{-1} \frac{c_i\,\omega}{\sqrt{1 - \omega^2}} + c \right]$$

$$\qquad (2\text{-}144)$$

$$= \cos z \qquad (2\text{-}145)$$

When n is an integer, $c = 0$ or $\pi$,[†] and $k_i = 2$, it may be shown [B2.103] that $F(\omega)$ has †

1. n poles at infinity; $\qquad\qquad\qquad\qquad\qquad$ (2-146)

2. poles at $\omega^2 = b_i{}^2$; $\qquad\qquad\qquad\qquad\qquad$ (2-147)

3. $n + 2q + 1$ equal ripples in the interval $-1 \leqslant \omega \leqslant 1$.   (2-148)

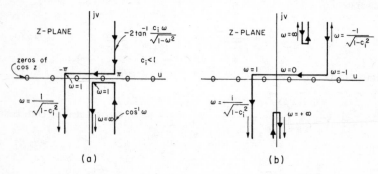

**Fig. 2-13.** (a) z-plane paths of $\cos^{-1} \omega$, $-2 \tan^{-1} \dfrac{c_i\omega}{1-\omega^2}$.
(b) Combined paths of (a).

We can visualize 1 and 3 by taking a walk in the z-plane (Eq. 2-145). Such a walk is shown in Figs. 2-13a and 2-13b for $n = 1$, $q = 1$. The equi-ripple property follows from the periodicity of $\cos z$ as z varies over the range $-q\,\pi \leqslant z \leqslant (q + n)\,\pi$ (Fig. 2-13b).

---

† The choice or 0 or $\pi$ will affect only the sign preceding $F(\omega)$. For convenience, we will assume c is chosen so that $\lim\limits_{\omega \to \infty} F(\omega) > 0$.

† These functions are known as Tchebycheff Rational Functions (TRF).

Several special cases of Equation 2.144 should be noted:

1. $q = 0$;  $F(\omega)$ is then the Tchebycheff polynomial.
2. $n = 0$;  $F(\omega)$ then approaches a constant as $\omega \rightarrow \infty$  (denoted by $H(\omega)$ in Fig. 2-12a). Note, however, that $H(\omega)$ need not be monotonic for $\omega^2 > 1$ (Fig. 2-12a might give this impression) if the poles $-b_i^2$ are chosen arbitrarily.

*Example 2.2:* Find an $F(\omega)$ which approximates zero and has poles at $\omega = \pm j1$, plus two poles at infinity.

Here,

$$F(\omega) = \cos\left(2 \cos^{-1} \omega - 2 \tan^{-1} \frac{\sqrt{2}\, \omega}{\sqrt{1-\omega^2}} + c\right) \quad (2\text{-}149)$$

$$F(\omega) = [\pm 1]\left[(2\omega^2 - 1)\left(\frac{1-3\omega^2}{\omega^2+1}\right) + (2\omega\sqrt{1-\omega^2})\right.$$
$$\left. \times \left(\frac{2\sqrt{2}\,\omega\sqrt{1-\omega^2}}{\omega^2+1}\right)\right] \quad (2\text{-}150)$$

$$= \frac{+11.66\,\omega^4 - 10.66\,\omega^2 + 1}{\omega^2+1}, \; c = \pi \quad (2\text{-}151)$$

which is equi-ripple over the interval $-1 \leqslant \omega \leqslant +1$.

*Equi-Ripple Approximation of Zero, Infinity.* The differential equation describing the characteristic of Fig. 2-12b may be derived pictorially in the same heuristic manner as Eq. 2-134.

$$\left(\frac{dF}{d\omega}\right)^2 - n^2 \frac{(1-F^2)\left[1 - \left(\frac{F}{F_0}\right)^2\right]}{(1-\omega^2)\left[1 - \left(\frac{\omega}{\omega_0}\right)^2\right]} L(\omega)$$

$$= 0 \begin{cases} F(0) = 0, \text{ F odd} \\ F(0) = \pm 1, \text{ F even} \end{cases} \quad (2\text{-}152)$$

We set $L(\omega) = 1$ and solve the resulting equation

$$\int \frac{dF}{\sqrt{[1-F^2]\left[1 - \left(\frac{F}{F_0}\right)^2\right]}}$$

$$= n \int \frac{d\omega}{\sqrt{[1 - \omega^2]\left[1 - \left(\dfrac{\omega}{\omega_0}\right)^2\right]}} + c \quad (2\text{-}153)$$

or (Table 2.3)

$$sn^{-1}\left(F; \frac{1}{F_0{}^2}\right) = n \; sn^{-1}\left(\omega; \frac{1}{\omega_0{}^2}\right) + c \quad (2\text{-}154)$$

so that

$$F = sn\left[n \; sn^{-1}\left(\omega; \frac{1}{\omega_0{}^2}\right) + c; \frac{1}{F_0{}^2}\right] \quad (2\text{-}155)$$

which is a rational function for any of the three conditions on n previously noted. However, only when

$$n = \frac{NK(m')}{K(m)} = \frac{K(m'_1)}{K(m_1)}, \; c = 0, \; N \text{ odd} \quad (2\text{-}156)$$

for $F(\omega)$ an odd function, or

$$n = \frac{NK(m')}{K(m)} = \frac{K(m_1')}{K(m_1)}, \; c = K(m'), \; N \text{ even}$$
$$(2\text{-}157)$$

for $F(\omega)$ even, is the resulting rational function equi-ripple, as is evident from another nz-plane walk (Figs. 2-14a and 2-14b). This time the equiripple property arises from the periodicity of sn (nz) in the intervals $- NK(m') \leqslant nz \leqslant NK(m') \; jK(m_1')-NK(m'_1) \leqslant nz \leqslant jK(m'_1) + NK(m')$ for N odd.

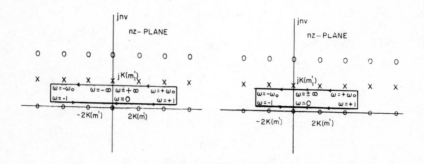

**Fig. 2-14.** NZ-plane path of $sn^{-1}$ $\omega$, Eq. 2-156 (a) N = 5; b() N = 4.

*Equi-Ripple Approximation of a Non-Zero Constant on an Internal Band by an Odd Function.* Equation 2-152 may also be solved to yield the characteristic of Fig. 2-12b provided that

$$n = \frac{NK(m_1')}{K(m_1)} = \frac{K(m')}{K(m)}, \quad c = 0 \qquad (2\text{-}158)$$

The walk is shown in Fig. 2-15. Note that the poles and zeros of $F(\omega)$ lie on the negative real axis.

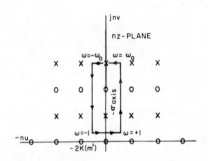

**Fig. 2-15.** NZ-plane path of $\mathrm{sn}^{-1}\,\omega$, Eq. 2-158, N = 3.

*Proof of Optimal Behavior.* Since Tchebycheff's theorem states a *necessary* condition for best approximation of a function, we have yet to show that the $F(\omega)$'s generated by Eqs. 2-144 and 2-155 are themselves optimum. We will now show that they are indeed the best approximation of zero and in what sense they are optimum.

*Theorem 2.1:* [B2.320] Of all even (odd) rational functions $P(\omega)$ with

1. q poles at $- b_i^2$                                                (2-159)

2. n poles at infinity                                                (2-160)

3. a maximum deviation, from zero, of $\epsilon$ where    (2-161)

$$|\epsilon| \leqslant 1 \qquad \omega^2 \leqslant 1 \qquad (2\text{-}162)$$

$F(\omega)$ of Eq. 2-144 has the property that

$$|F(\omega)| \geqslant |P(\omega)| \qquad \omega^2 > 1 \qquad (2\text{-}163)$$

*Proof:* Since $|P(\omega)| \leqslant 1$ for $\omega^2 < 1$, the difference

$$B(\omega) = F(\omega) - P(\omega) \qquad (2\text{-}164)$$

has the property

$$F(\omega_i) = +1 \qquad \text{implies } B(\omega_i) \geqslant 0 \qquad (2\text{-}165)$$

$$F(\omega_i) = -1 \qquad \text{implies } B(\omega_i) \leqslant 0 \qquad (2\text{-}166)$$

Also, since extrema of $F(\omega)$ occur at $\omega = \pm 1$, we have

$$|F(\pm 1)| \geqslant |P(\pm 1)| \qquad (2\text{-}167)$$

Now assume the following cases:

*Case I:* Equations 2-165 - 2-167 are not met with the equality sign at any $\omega_1$. Since $F(\omega)$ achieves the value $\pm 1$ alternately a total of $n + 2q + 1$ times in the interval $(-1 \leqslant \omega \leqslant +1)$, $B(\omega)$ becomes positive and negative alternately $n + 2q + 1$ times and therefore must have a total of at least $n + 2q$ zeros in this interval. If, for some $\omega_2 > 1$

$$|P(\pm \omega_2)| \geqslant |(F \pm \omega_2)| \qquad (2\text{-}168)$$

there then exists an $\omega_1$ $(1 < \omega_1 \leqslant \omega_2)$ such that $B(\pm \omega_1) = 0$ (Fig. 2-16a). But this would require $B(\omega)$ to have $n + 2q + 2$ zeros, which is impossible since both $P(\omega)$ and $F(\omega)$ have the same denominators and have numerators of degree $n + 2q$. Hence, no such $\omega_2$ exists.

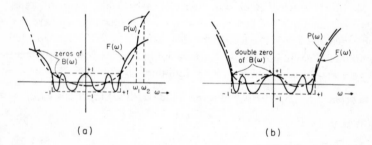

(a)                              (b)

**Fig. 2-16.** Illustration of optimality proof.

*Case II:* Of Eqs. 2-165 - 2-167, one or more are satisfied by the equality sign. Then $dB(\omega_i)/d\omega = 0$ and $B(\omega_i)$ must have at least a double zero at $\omega_i$. Hence, the required number of zeros of $B(\omega)$ is unchanged from Case I by this degeneracy.

The proof of the theorem follows.

*Theorem 2.2:* Of all even (odd) rational functions $P(\omega)$ with

(1) a numerator of degree $N_1$ and a denominator of degree $N_2$ where

$$N_2 \leqslant N, \ N_1 \leqslant N; \qquad\qquad (2\text{-}169)$$

(2) a maximum deviation from zero of $\epsilon$ where

$$\epsilon \leqslant 1 \qquad \omega^2 \leqslant 1 \qquad\qquad (2\text{-}170)$$

the $F(\omega)$ of Eq. 2-155 of order N has the largest minimum deviation $(F_0)$ from zero for $\omega^2 \geqslant \omega_0^2$ when $\omega_0$ is given.

*Proof:* Left to the reader. (Hint: Note that $P(\omega)$ may have *any* N (or less) poles, requiring a count of the zeros of $B(\omega)$ in the regions $(-\infty \leqslant \omega \leqslant \omega_0)$, $(-1 \leqslant \omega \leqslant +1)$, and $(+\omega_0 \leqslant \omega \leqslant +\infty)$.

*Theorem 2.3:* Theorem 2.2 is changed to read "the $F(\omega)$ of Eq. 2-155 has the smallest $\omega_0$ for a given minimum deviation from zero $(F_0)$ for $\omega^2 \geqslant \omega_0^2$."

## PROBLEMS

2.1. Find (to three significant figures):

   (a) $sn(.51;.36)$                      (c) $cd\ (.6 + j.5;.7)$

   (b) $cn\left(\dfrac{K(m)}{3};.6\right)$

2.2. Find (approximately):

   (a) $cn\ (.7;.98)$                    (b) $sc\left(\dfrac{K(m)}{7};.01\right)$

   (c) $\dfrac{K(m)}{K(m_1)}$ if           (d) $m_1$, if $\dfrac{K(m_1)}{K(m)} = 20$

      1) $m = .7$:

      2) $m = .99$

2.3. Consider the function

$$P(s) = sn\ [n\ sn^{-1}\ (\omega;m);m']\Big|_{\omega = \frac{s}{j}}$$

If

$$n = \frac{NK(m_1')}{K(m_1)} = \frac{K(m')}{K(m)}$$

answer the following:

(a) How many zeros has $P(s)$ on the $\omega$-axis? $\sigma$-axis?

(b) For $m = \frac{1}{4}$, $N = 5$, find all the zeros of $P(s)$. Repeat (a) and (b) for

$$n = \frac{NK(m')}{K(m)} = \frac{K(m_1')}{K(m_1)}$$

2.4. Show that: (a) $\operatorname{sn}\left[\dfrac{NK(m')}{K(m)}z;m'\right] = \operatorname{sn} z \displaystyle\prod_{r=1}^{\frac{N-1}{2}}$

$$\times \frac{\operatorname{sn}^2 z - \operatorname{sn}^2 \dfrac{2rK(m)}{N}}{1 - m\left[\operatorname{sn}^2 z\ \operatorname{sn}^2 \dfrac{2rK(m)}{N}\right]}$$

(b) $\operatorname{cn}\left[\dfrac{NK(m')}{K(m)}z;m'\right] = \operatorname{cn} z \displaystyle\prod_{r=1}^{\frac{N-1}{2}}$

$$\times \frac{\operatorname{cn}^2 z - \operatorname{dn}^2 z\ \operatorname{sn}^2 \dfrac{2rK(m)}{N}}{1 - m\left[\operatorname{sn}^2 z\ \operatorname{sn}^2 \dfrac{2rK(m)}{N}\right]}$$

(c) $\operatorname{dn}\left[\dfrac{NK(m')}{K(m)}z;m'\right] = \operatorname{dn} z \displaystyle\prod_{r=1}^{\frac{N-1}{2}}$

$$\times \frac{\operatorname{dn}^2 z - m\ \operatorname{cn}^2 z\ \operatorname{sn}^2 \dfrac{2rK(m)}{N}}{1 - m\left[\operatorname{sn}^2 z\ \operatorname{sn}^2 \dfrac{2rK(m)}{N}\right]}$$

where

$$\frac{NK(m')}{K(m)} = \frac{K(m_1')}{K(m_1)}, \quad N \text{ odd}$$

and

$$\operatorname{sn} z = \operatorname{sn} (z;m), \text{ etc.}$$

show for N even

$$\text{sn}\left[\frac{NK(m')}{K(m)}\ z;m'\right] = \prod_{r=1}^{\frac{N}{2}}$$

$$\times \frac{\text{sn}^2z - \text{sn}^2\ \dfrac{(2r-1)\,K(m)}{N}}{1 - m\left[\text{sn}^2z\ \text{sn}^2\ \dfrac{(2r-1)\,K(m)}{N}\right]}$$

$$\text{cn}\left[\frac{NK(m')}{K(m)}\ z;m'\right] = \prod_{r=1}^{\frac{N}{2}}$$

$$\times \frac{\text{cn}^2z - \text{dn}^2z\ \text{sn}^2\ \dfrac{(2r-1)\,K(m)}{N}}{1 - m\left[\text{sn}^2z\ \text{sn}^2\ \dfrac{(2r-1)\,K(m)}{N}\right]}$$

$$\text{dn}\left[\frac{NK(m')}{K(m)}\ z;m'\right] = \prod_{r=1}^{\frac{N}{2}}$$

$$\times \frac{\text{dn}^2z - m\ \text{cn}^2z\ \text{sn}^2\ \dfrac{(2r-1)\,K(m)}{N}}{1 - m\left[\text{sn}^2z\ \text{sn}^2\ \dfrac{2r+1)\,K(m)}{N}\right]}$$

2.5. Use Tchebycheff's theorem to show that of all polynomials of degree n, with unity leading coefficient, the Tchebycheff polynomial has the smallest deviation from zero. (Hint: Re-state the problem so that $f(\omega) = \omega^n$.)

2.6. Find an $F(\omega)$ with poles at $\omega^2 = 1 \pm j1$ such that $F(\omega)$ deviates least from zero in the interval $[-1, +1]$. (Let both numerator and denominator have unity leading coefficient.)

2.7. Prove Theorem 2.2.

2.8. Prove Theorem 2.3.

2.9. By letting Eq. 2-152 be of the form

$$\left(\frac{dF}{d\omega}\right)^2 - \frac{k^2(F_0{}^2 - F^2)}{(\omega_0{}^2 - \omega^2)}\ L(\omega) = 0$$

show that the equi-ripple response converges to the maximally flat response as $F_0 \to 0$, $\omega_0 \to 0$. Do this
  (a) for $L(\omega) = 1$

(b) for $L(\omega) = \dfrac{Q^2(\omega^2)}{P_2(\omega^2)}$

when Q is of no higher degree than P. (Hint: The general form of the maximally flat response is $F(\omega^2) = \omega^m/P(\omega)$.)

## TABLE 2-1: Important Values of Elliptic Functions

| $\overset{z\,\rightarrow}{f(z)}$ | 0 | $K(m)$ | $2K(m)$ | $jK(m_1)$ | $2jK(m_1)$ | $K(m)$ $+jK(m_1)$ | $2K(m)$ $+2jK(m_1)$ |
|---|---|---|---|---|---|---|---|
| sn z | 0 | 1 | 0 | $\infty$ | 0 | $m^{-1/2}$ | 0 |
| cn z | 1 | 0 | $-1$ | $\infty$ | $-1$ | $-j\left(\dfrac{m_1}{m}\right)^{1/2}$ | 1 |
| dn z | 1 | $m_1^{1/2}$ | 1 | $\infty$ | $-1$ | 0 | $-1$ |
| sc z | 0 | $\infty$ | 0 | $j1$ | 0 | $j\left(\dfrac{1}{m_1}\right)^{1/2}$ | 0 |
| ds z | $\infty$ | $m_1^{1/2}$ | $\infty$ | $-jm^{1/2}$ | $\infty$ | 0 | $\infty$ |
| dc z | 1 | $\infty$ | $-1$ | $m^{1/2}$ | 1 | 0 | $-1$ |

## TABLE 2-2

$$\text{sn }(jz;m) = j \text{ sc }(z;m_1)$$
$$\text{dn }(jz;m) = \text{dc }(z;m_1)$$
$$\text{cn }(jz;m) = \text{nc }(z;m_1)$$

## TABLE 2-3

$$\int \frac{d\omega}{\left\{\left[1 - \left(\frac{\omega}{a}\right)^2\right](1 - \omega^2)\right\}^{1/2}} = sn^{-1}\left(\omega; \frac{1}{a^2}\right) + C$$

$$\int \frac{d\omega}{\left\{\left[1 + \left(\frac{\omega}{a}\right)^2\right](1 - \omega^2)\right\}^{1/2}} = \frac{a}{(1 + a^2)^{1/2}} \, cn^{-1}$$

$$\times \left(\omega; \frac{1}{a^2 + 1}\right) + C$$

$$\int \frac{d\omega}{\left\{\left[1 - \left(\frac{\omega}{a}\right)^2\right](1 - \omega^2)\right\}^{1/2}} = ja \, dn^{-1} \, (\omega; 1 - a^2) + C$$

$$\int \frac{d\omega}{\left\{\left[1 + \left(\frac{\omega}{a}\right)^2\right](1 - \omega^2)\right\}^{1/2}} = sc^{-1}\left(\omega; \frac{a^2 - 1}{a^2}\right) + C$$

$$\int \frac{d\omega}{\left\{\left[1 + \left(\frac{\omega}{a}\right)^2\right](1 - \omega^2)\right\}^{1/2}} = j \, \frac{a}{(1 + a^2)^{1/2}}$$

$$\times ds^{-1}\left[\frac{\omega}{(1 + a^2)^{1/2}}; \frac{a^2}{1 + a^2}\right] + C$$

$$\int \frac{d\omega}{\left\{\left[1 - \left(\frac{\omega}{a}\right)^2\right](1 - \omega^2)\right\}^{1/2}} = dc^{-1}\left(\omega; \frac{1}{a^2}\right) + C$$

**TABLE 2-4**

| ARGUMENT | sn | cn | dn |
|---|---|---|---|
| $z$ | sn $z$ | cn $z$ | dn $z$ |
| $-z$ | $-$sn $z$ | cn $z$ | dn $z$ |
| $z \pm 2K(m)$ | $-$sn $z$ | $-$cn $z$ | dn $z$ |
| $z \pm 2jK(m)$ | sn $z$ | $-$cn $z$ | $-$dn $z$ |
| $z \pm 2K(m) \pm 2jK(m_1)$ | $-$sn $z$ | cn $z$ | $-$dn $z$ |
| $z \pm K(m)$ | $\pm$cd $z$ | $\mp m_1^{1/2}$sd $z$ | $m_1^{1/2}$ nd $z$ |
| $z \pm jK(m_1)$ | $\pm m^{-1/2}$ ns $z$ | $\mp jm^{-1/2}$ds $z$ | $\mp j$ cs $z$ |

**TABLE 2-5**

$$sn(z_1 + z_2) = (s_1c_2d_2 + s_2c_1d_1)/D$$
$$cn(z_1 + z_2) = (c_1c_2 - s_1d_1s_2d_2)/D$$
$$dn(z_1 + z_2) = (d_1d_2 - ms_1c_1s_2c_2)/D$$
$$sn(z_1 + z_2) \, sn(z_1 - z_2) = (s_1^2 - s_2^2)/D$$
$$cn(z_1 + z_2) \, cn(z_1 - z_2) = (c_1^2 - s_2^2 \, d_1^2)/D$$
$$dn(z_1 + z_2) \, dn(z_1 - z_2) = (d_1^2 - mc_1^2s_1^2)/D$$

where $D = 1 - ms_1^2s_2^2$

$$s_1 = sn(z_1, \ m)$$
$$s_2 = sn(z_2, \ m)$$

etc.

# 3

## EQUI-RIPPLE APPROXIMATION OF NETWORK RESPONSES

Having a knowledge of the form of rational circular and elliptic functions as well as their approximating properties, we examine this application in obtaining functions approximating certain "ideal" network responses. In particular, well-known filter design formulae are derived, examples are given, and realization of the filters is discussed briefly.

### 3.1. Magnitude Function

To obtain a low-pass characteristic similar to Fig. 3-1 from the equiripple functions of Fig. 2-12a, we can form either [B2.319]

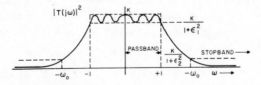

**Fig. 3-1.** Low-pass magnitude approximation.

47

$$|T(j\omega)|^2 = \frac{1}{1 + \epsilon' F(\omega)} \tag{3-1}$$

or

$$= 1 - \epsilon'' H(\omega) \tag{3-2}$$

where

$$F(\omega) = \cos\left(2n \cos^{-1} \omega - 2 \sum \tan^{-1} \frac{c_i\omega}{\sqrt{1 - \omega^2}} + c\right) \tag{3-3}$$

$$H(\omega) = \left(2 \sum \tan^{-1} \frac{c_i \omega}{\sqrt{1 - \omega^2}} + c\right) \tag{3-4}$$

(as discussed in Chapter 2) and $\epsilon''$ is chosen so that $|T(j\omega)|^2 \geqslant 0$ for all $\omega$. Since the poles of either $F(\omega)$ or $H(\omega)$ can be picked in advance, the choice of poles or zeros depends on whether the poles or the zeros of $|T(j\omega)|^2$ are presented [B2.316]. In any case, the resulting filter characteristic has the sharpest cutoff (in the sense of Theorem 2.1) for a given passband tolerance of a function of like degree with the chosen poles (zeros).

If we do not pre-select the poles or zeros of $T(s)$, we may choose

$$|T(j\omega)|^2 = \frac{1}{1 + \epsilon F^2(\omega)} \tag{3-5}$$

where

$$F(\omega) = sn \; [n \; sn^{-1} \; (\omega;m);m] \tag{3-6}$$

$$= sn \; nz \tag{3-7}$$

(as given in Section 2.4). The nz-plane root locus (as a function of $\epsilon$) of the poles of $|T(j\omega)|^2$ is then shown in Fig. 3-2. From Theorems 2.2 and 2.3, for a function having the same *number* of poles, the elliptic characteristic has the best combination of (1) passband and (2) stop-band tolerances, and (3) the smallest transition region ($\omega_0$). Any one of these can be enhanced at the expense of one or both of the others. Note that to achieve this optimality, $|T(j\omega)|^2$ is equi-ripple in both passband and stopband.

**Design Formulae and Example.** We now derive the elliptic formulae necessary to obtain the magnitude characteristic of Fig. 3-1. First we note (Eq. 3-5)

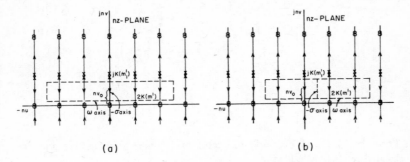

**Fig. 3-2.** Root locus of poles of $|T(j\omega)|^2$.

$$|T(j\omega)|^2 = \frac{1}{1 + \epsilon \, \mathrm{sn}^2 \, (nz + c;m')} \qquad (3\text{-}8)$$

where

$$z = \mathrm{sn}^{-1} \, (\omega;m) \qquad (3\text{-}9)$$

$$m = \frac{1}{\omega_0{}^2} \qquad (3\text{-}10)$$

and where n, N, and C are given as in Eqs. 2-156 and 2-157. Also, since

$$z \, \big|_{\omega = \pm 1} = \mathrm{sn}^{-1} \, (\pm 1;m) \qquad (3\text{-}11)$$

$$= \pm \, K(m) \qquad (3\text{-}12)$$

it follows that

$$|T(\pm j1)|^2 = \frac{1}{1 + \epsilon \, \mathrm{sn}^2 \left[ \pm \dfrac{NK(m')}{K(m)} \times K(m) + c;m' \right]} \qquad (3\text{-}13)$$

$$= \frac{1}{1 + \epsilon} \qquad (3\text{-}14)$$

Thus $K = 1$ (Fig. 3-1), $\epsilon = \epsilon_1{}^2$. Also, we recall that

$$z \, \big|_{\omega = \pm \omega_0} = \pm \, K(m) \pm j \, K(m_1) \qquad (3\text{-}15)$$

so that

$$|T(\pm j\omega_0)|^2 = \frac{1}{1 + \epsilon_1^2 \left(\dfrac{1}{m'}\right)} \tag{3-16}$$

and

$$\epsilon_2^2 = \frac{\epsilon_1^2}{m'} \tag{3-17}$$

From Eq. 3-8 and Fig. 3-2, the zeros of $|T(j\omega)|^2$ are double and are located at (for N odd)†

$$nz_r = \pm rK(m') + jK(m'_1) \quad r = 0, 2, \ldots, N - 1 \tag{3-18}$$

or

$$sn^{-1}\left(\frac{z_r}{j};m\right) = \pm \frac{rK(m')}{n} + j\frac{K(m_1')}{n} \tag{3-19}$$

$$= \pm \frac{r}{N} K(m) + jK(m_1) \tag{3-20}$$

Therefore, we have

$$z_r = jsn\left[\pm \frac{r}{N} K(m) + jK(m_1);m\right] \tag{3-21}$$

or

$$z_r = \frac{\pm j}{(m^{1/2})\left[sn \dfrac{r}{N} K(m;m)\right]} \tag{3-22}$$

from Table 2.4. The poles are located (from Fig. 3-2) at

$$np_r = \pm rK(m') + j n v_0 \quad r = 0, 2, \ldots N - 1 \tag{3-23}$$

or

$$p_r = jsn\left[\pm \frac{r}{N} K(m) + jv_0;m\right] \tag{3-24}$$

To find $v_0$, we note

$$1 + \epsilon_1^2 sn^2 \left[\pm r K(m') + j nv_0;m'\right] = 0 \tag{3-25}$$

---

† The case for N even is left as an exercise.

or

$$1 + \epsilon_1^2 \, \text{sn}^2 \, (j \, nv_0; m') = 0 \qquad (3\text{-}26)$$

from Table 2.3, so that

$$1 - \epsilon_1^2 \, \text{sc}^2 \, (nv_0; m'_1) = 0 \qquad (3\text{-}27)$$

$$v_0 = \frac{1}{n} \, \text{sc}^{-1} \left( \frac{1}{\epsilon_1}; m'_1 \right) \qquad (3\text{-}28)$$

The design procedure is the following (given $\omega_0$, $\epsilon_1$, $\epsilon_2$):

1. Calculate $m = \dfrac{1}{\omega_0^2}$ \qquad\qquad\qquad\qquad (3-29)

$$m' = \left( \frac{\epsilon_1}{\epsilon_2} \right)^2 \qquad (3\text{-}30)$$

2. Determine the degree of the approximating function by choosing the smallest integral $N$ that satisfies

$$N \geqslant \frac{K(m_1')}{K(m_1)} \, \frac{K(m)}{K(m')} \qquad (3\text{-}31)$$

From $m$ near 1, $m'$ near zero, we obtain, from Eq. 2-64, the approximate formula

$$N \geqslant \frac{2}{\pi^2} \ln \frac{4\epsilon_2}{\epsilon_1} \ln \frac{8}{\omega_0 - 1} \qquad (3\text{-}32)$$

3. Determine the zeros and poles of $T(s)$ by formulae

$$z_r = \frac{\pm j}{(m^{1/2}) \left[ \text{sn} \, \dfrac{r}{N} \, K(m); m \right]} \qquad (3\text{-}33)$$

$$p_r = j \, \text{sn} \left[ \pm \frac{r}{N} \, K(m) + j \, v_0; m \right] \qquad (3\text{-}34)$$

where

$$r = 0, 2, \ldots, N - 1 \qquad N \text{ odd} \qquad (3\text{-}35)$$

$$r = 1, 3, \ldots, N - 1 \qquad N \text{ even} \qquad (3\text{-}36)$$

$$v_0 = \frac{K(m)}{NK(m')} \, \text{sc}^{-1} \left( \frac{1}{\epsilon_1}; m'_1 \right) \qquad (3\text{-}37)$$

$$\approx \frac{K(m)}{NK(m')} \sinh^{-1} \frac{1}{\epsilon_1} \qquad (3\text{-}38)$$

from m' near zero.

*Example 3.1:*   Passband Spec.:    2 db ripple, $0 \leqslant \omega \leqslant 1$   (3-39)

Stopband Spec.:   25 db min., $1.33 \leqslant \omega \leqslant \infty$   (3-40)

$$m = .566 \qquad (3\text{-}41)$$

$$\epsilon_1 = .765 \qquad (3\text{-}42)$$

$$\epsilon_2 = 161 \qquad (3\text{-}43)$$

If we estimate N, we find, since m' is near zero,

$$N \geqslant \frac{2}{\pi} \left[ \ln \frac{4\epsilon_2}{\epsilon_1} \right] \left[ \frac{K(m)}{K(m_1)} \right] = 2.98 \qquad (3\text{-}44)$$

Choosing $N = 3$, we calculate the pole and zero locations

$$z_1 = \frac{\pm j}{(.75) \ \mathrm{sn} \left[ \dfrac{2K(m)}{3} ; .566 \right]} \qquad (3\text{-}45)$$

$$= \pm j \ 1.47 \qquad (3\text{-}46)$$

$$v_0 = \frac{1.909}{3 \times \dfrac{\pi}{2}} \ \sinh^{-1} \frac{1}{.765} = .438 \qquad (3\text{-}47)$$

$$p_1 = j \ \mathrm{sn} \ (j.438,.566) = - \ \mathrm{sc} \ (.438,.434) \qquad (3\text{-}48)$$

$$= - \ .463 \qquad (3\text{-}49)$$

$$p_2 = j \ \mathrm{sn} \left[ \frac{\pm 2K(m)}{3} + j \ .438; .566 \right] \qquad (3\text{-}50)$$

$$= -.129 \pm j \ .962 \qquad (3\text{-}51)$$

from Example 2.1. The resulting transfer function is then:

$$T(s) = \frac{(s^2 + 2.16)}{s^3 + .721s^2 + 1.061s + .437}$$

The resultant magnitude function is shown in Fig. 3-3.

Although the advantage of the elliptic filter is small in such a simple case, to meet the rigid requirements (for example)

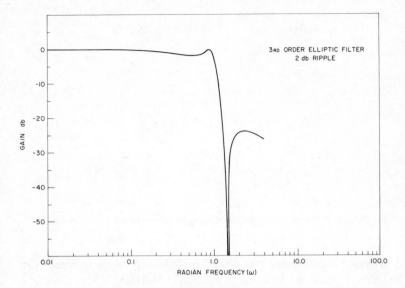

**Fig. 3-3.** Magnitude response of elliptic filter example.

Passband:        $\frac{1}{2}$ db ripple   $0 \leqslant \omega \leqslant 1$        (3-52)

Stopband:        80 db down   $1.03 \leqslant \omega \leqslant \infty$        (3-53)

requires (from Problem 3.10)

$$N_E = 14 \qquad N_{TCH} = 45 \qquad N_{BUT} = 350 \qquad (3-54)$$

requiring 20, 45, and 350 reactive elements, respectively. The advantage of the elliptic filter is now clear.

## 3.2. Phase Function

Since any odd rational function qualifies as an angle function (Chapter 1), the choice of $A(\omega)$ of the form of Eqs. 2-155 and 2-158 will yield the approximation of a non-zero phase in an internal band (Fig. 3-4a). The nz-plane root locus of the expression

$$1 + j \, \epsilon \, \text{sn} \, (nz;m') = 0 \qquad (3-55)$$

(as given in Chapter 2), from which the zeros and poles of $T(s)$ can be determined, is shown in Fig. 3-4b.

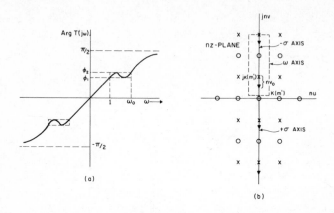

**Fig. 3-4.** (a) Phase response; (b) Root locus of phase function $[1+j\epsilon A(\omega)\omega]$.

*Design Formulae and Example.* The following design formulae may be derived from the formulae of Section 3.3. Refer to Fig. 3-4 for a definition of constants.

1. Calculate: $\quad m = \dfrac{1}{\omega_0^{\,2}}$ $\qquad\qquad\qquad\qquad$ (3-56)

$$m' = \left(\frac{\tan\ \phi_1}{\tan\ \phi_2}\right)^2 \qquad\qquad\qquad (3\text{-}57)$$

2. Obtain the degree of the approximating function from

$$N = \frac{K(m_1)Km')}{K(m'_1)K(m)} \qquad\qquad\qquad (3\text{-}58)$$

$$\approx \frac{\pi^2}{2}\ \ln\ \frac{16}{m'_1}\ \ln\ 4\omega_0 \qquad\qquad (3\text{-}59)$$

for m near 0, m' near 1

3. Determine the zeros and poles of $T(s)$ by the formulae

$$z_r = -sc\left[\frac{r}{N}\ K(m_1) - v_0;m_1\right] \quad r = 1, 3, \ldots, N, \quad N \text{ odd}$$

$$\ldots, N-1, N \text{ even}$$

$$(3\text{-}60)$$

$$p_r = -sc \left[ \frac{r}{N} K(m_1) + v_0;m_1 \right] \quad r = 1, 3, \ldots, N-2, \text{ N odd}$$

$$\ldots, N-1, \text{ N even}$$

$$(3\text{-}61)$$

where

$$v_0 = \frac{K(m_1)}{NK(m'_1)} \, sc^{-1} \left( \frac{\tan \phi_1}{m'^{1/2}};m'_1 \right) \qquad (3\text{-}62)$$

For $m_1 \approx 0$,

$$v_0 \approx \frac{2K(m_1)}{N\pi} \, \tan^{-1} \left( \frac{\tan \phi_1}{m'^{1/2}} \right) \qquad (3\text{-}63)$$

*Example 3.2:* It is desired to approximate a constant phase of $-45° \pm .5°$ from $\omega = 1$ to $\omega = 2$. In this case,

$$m = \tfrac{1}{4} \quad m' = .9326 \quad m'_1 = .0674 \quad N \geqslant 2.26 \quad (3\text{-}64)$$

Choosing $N = 3$, $v_0 = -.3625$, we find

$$T(s) = \frac{(s + 1.402)}{(s + .3680)(s + 5.391)} \qquad (3\text{-}65)$$

The plot of $B(\omega)$ is shown in Fig. 3-5. For an application of such approximation, see Problem 3.9.

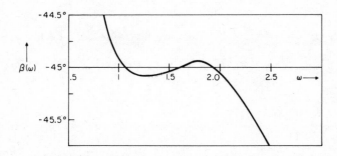

**Fig. 3-5.** Example of constant phase response.

### 3.3. Delay Function†

Consider the possibility of forming an equi-ripple delay function approximating a constant $(0 \leqslant \omega \leqslant 1)$ from the equation

$$D_f(\omega) = \tau - \epsilon H(\omega) \tag{3-66}$$

where $H(\omega)$ is as previously defined (Eq. 3-4). From Chapter 1, we require that (assuming $T(s)$ to be an all-pole function)

$$\tau - \epsilon H(\omega) = - \sum \frac{p_i}{\omega^2 + p_i^2} \tag{3-67}$$

or

$$\text{Residue } [-\epsilon H(\omega)] = -p_i \tag{3-68}$$
$$-p_i^2$$

Therefore, we first find the residue of $H(\omega)$ at a sample pole $-p_k^2$.
To begin, we define

$$B(\omega) = \cos^{-1} \sqrt{\frac{1 - c_k^2}{2}} \ \omega \tag{3-69}$$

$$C(\omega) = \sum_{i \neq k} \tan^{-1} \frac{c_i \omega}{\sqrt{1 - \omega^2}} \tag{3-70}$$

$$D(\omega) = \tan^{-1} \frac{c_k \omega}{\sqrt{1 - \omega^2}}$$

where $p_k^2 = 1/(c_k^2 - 1)$. Then, we may solve Eq. 3-69 to yield

$$\cos 2B = (1 - c_k^2) \ \omega^2 - 1 \tag{3-71}$$

so that

$$\text{Res } [-\epsilon H(\omega)]$$
$$-p_k^2$$
$$= \frac{-\epsilon}{1 - c_k^2} \lim {}_{\omega^2 \to -1/(c_k^2 - 1)} [\cos 2 B \cos (2C + 2D)] \tag{3-72}$$

---

† See [B2.419, 2.423, 2.427, 2.430].

We may now readily show the following:

1. $\cos 2B \cos (2C + 2D) = (\cos 2B \cos 2D) \cos 2C$

$\qquad - \sqrt{\cos^2 2B - (\cos 2B \cos 2D)^2} \sin 2C$ $\qquad\qquad$ (3-73)

2. $\cos 2B \cos 2D = \cos^2 (B + D) - \sin^2 (B - D)$ $\qquad\qquad$ (3-74)

$$= \cos^2 \left( \cos^{-1} \frac{1 - c_k^2}{2} \omega + \tan^{-1} \frac{c_k \omega}{\sqrt{1 - \omega^2}} \right)$$

$$- \sin^2 \left( \cos^{-1} \frac{1 - c_k^2}{2} \omega - \tan^{-1} \frac{c_k \omega}{\sqrt{1 - \omega^2}} \right)$$

$$(3-75)$$

$$= \omega^2 (1 + c_k^2) - 1 \qquad\qquad (3-76)$$

3. $\qquad \lim_{\omega^2 \to -1/(c_k^2 - 1)} \cos 2B \cos 2D = \dfrac{2c_k^2}{1 - c_k^2}$

$$(3-77)$$

4. $\qquad \lim_{\omega^2 \to -1/(c_k^2 - 1)} \cos 2C = \sum_{i \neq k}^{q} \tan^{-1} \dfrac{jc_i}{c_k}$

$$(3-78)$$

5. $\qquad \lim_{\omega^2 \to -1/(c_k^2 - 1)} \cos 2B = 0 \qquad\qquad (3-79)$

Equation 3-72, therefore, becomes

$$\begin{aligned} \operatorname*{Res}_{-p_k^2} = \frac{-\epsilon}{(1 - c_k^2)} &\left[ \cos 2 \left( \sum_{i \neq k}^{q} \tan^{-1} \frac{jc_i}{c_k} \right) \left( \frac{2c_k^2}{1 - c_k^2} \right) \right. \\ &\left. -j \left( \sin 2 \sum_{i \neq k}^{q} \tan^{-1} \frac{jc_i}{c_k} \right) \left( \frac{2c_k^2}{1 - c_k^2} \right) \right] \end{aligned}$$ $\quad$ (3-80)

$$= -\frac{2\epsilon c_k^2}{(1 - c_k^2)^2} \exp \left( -2j \sum_{i \neq k}^{q} \tan^{-1} \frac{jc_i}{c_k} \right) \quad (3\text{-}81)$$

$$= -\frac{2\epsilon c_k^2}{(1 - c_k^2)^2} \exp \left( -\sum_{i \neq k}^{q} \ln \frac{1 - c_i/c_k}{1 + c_i/c_k} \right) \quad (3\text{-}82)$$

$$= -\frac{2\epsilon c_k^2}{(1 - c_k^2)^2} \mathop{\pi}_{i \neq k}^{q} \frac{c_k + c_i}{c_k - c_i} \qquad (3\text{-}83)$$

## TABLE 3-1

$$T(s) = \frac{1}{P(s)} = \frac{1}{1 + a_1 s + \cdots + s^n}$$

### ± 2% (± .002 second) ripple

| n | $\omega_c$ | $a_1$ | $a_2$ $\times 10^{-3}$ | $a_3$ $\times 10^{-4}$ | $a_4$ $\times 10^{-5}$ | $a_5$ $\times 10^{-1}$ | $a_6$ $\times 10^{-1}$ | $a_7$ $\times 10^{-2}$ | $a_8$ $\times 10^{-6}$ | $a_9$ $\times 10^{-7}$ | $a_{10}$ $\times 10^{-8}$ |
|---|---|---|---|---|---|---|---|---|---|---|---|
| 1. | .06318 | 1.0020 | | | | | | | | | |
| 2. | .61284 | .99800 | 3.4708 | | | | | | | | |
| 3. | 1.5482 | 1.0020 | 4.0531 | .76596 | | | | | | | |
| 4. | 2.6795 | .99800 | 4.3648 | 1.0054 | 1.2565 | | | | | | |
| 5. | 3.9202 | 1.0020 | 4.4930 | 1.1780 | 1.7962 | 1.6502 | | | | | |
| 6. | 5.2290 | .99800 | 4.6060 | 1.2575 | 2.2703 | 2.4973 | 1.7999 | | | | |
| 7. | 6.5836 | 1.0020 | 4.6566 | 1.3351 | 2.5284 | 3.4040 | 2.8558 | 1.6899 | | | |
| 8. | 7.9708 | .99800 | 4.7147 | 1.3711 | 2.7739 | 3.9224 | 4.1485 | 2.7599 | 1.3748 | | |
| 9. | 9.3829 | 1.0020 | 4.7411 | 1.4169 | 2.9193 | 4.4790 | 4.9619 | 4.2771 | 2.3223 | .99913 | |
| 10. | 10.813 | .99800 | 4.7771 | 1.4354 | 3.0694 | 4.8037 | 5.8579 | 5.2596 | 3.7975 | 1.7206 | .65068 |

### ± 1% (± .01 second) ripple

| n | $\omega_c$ | $a_1$ | $a_2$ | $a_3$ | $a_4$ | $a_5$ |
|---|---|---|---|---|---|---|
| 1. | .14073 | 1.0100 | | | | |
| 2. | .91076 | .99000 | 3.6317 | | | |
| 3. | 2.0151 | 1.0100 | 4.0453 | .84090 | | |
| 4. | 3.2676 | .99000 | 4.4817 | 1.0039 | 1.4214 | |
| 5. | 4.5996 | 1.0100 | 4.4862 | 1.2151 | 1.8166 | 1.9309 |

## TABLE 3-1 (cont.)

$$T(s) = \frac{1}{P(s)} = \frac{1}{1 + a_1 s + \dots + s^n}$$

±1% (±.01 second) ripple, cont.

| n | $\omega_c$ | $a_1$ | $a_2$ $\times 10^{-3}$ | $a_3$ $\times 10^{-4}$ | $a_4$ $\times 10^{-5}$ | $a_5$ $\times 10^{-1}$ | $a_6$ $\times 10^{-1}$ | $a_7$ $\times 10^{-2}$ | $a_8$ $\times 10^{-6}$ | $a_9$ $\times 10^{-7}$ | $a_{10}$ $\times 10^{-8}$ |
|---|---|---|---|---|---|---|---|---|---|---|---|
| 6. | 5.9805 | .99000 | 4.6343 | 1.2506 | 2.3592 | 2.5265 | 2.1388 | 2.0525 | | | |
| 7. | 7.3940 | 1.0100 | 4.6503 | 1.3614 | 2.5398 | 3.6100 | 2.9264 | 2.8245 | 1.6881 | | |
| 8. | 8.8309 | .99000 | 4.7339 | 1.3616 | 2.8303 | 3.9281 | 4.4272 | 4.6540 | 2.4054 | 1.2509 | |
| 9. | 10.285 | 1.0100 | 4.7354 | 1.4385 | 2.9520 | 4.6389 | 5.0234 | 4.6540 | 4.1510 | 1.7775 | |
| 10. | 11.753 | .99000 | 4.7910 | 1.4295 | 3.1090 | 4.7903 | 6.0734 | 5.3077 | 4.1510 | 1.7775 | .81757 |

±5% (±.05 second) ripple

| n | $\omega_c$ | $a_1$ | $a_2$ | $a_3$ | $a_4$ | $a_5$ | $a_6$ | $a_7$ | $a_8$ | $a_9$ | $a_{10}$ |
|---|---|---|---|---|---|---|---|---|---|---|---|
| 1. | .30899 | 1.0500 | | | | | | | | | |
| 2. | 1.3438 | .95000 | 3.9453 | | | | | | | | |
| 3. | 2.6159 | 1.0500 | 3.9643 | .98531 | | | | | | | |
| 4. | 3.9835 | .98000 | 4.5234 | .95178 | 1.6675 | | | | | | |
| 5. | 5.4014 | 1.0500 | 4.4290 | 1.0309 | 1.7824 | 2.3988 | | | | | |
| 6. | 6.8502 | .95000 | 4.6900 | 1.1892 | 2.4964 | 2.3973 | 2.6125 | | | | |
| 7. | 8.3198 | 1.0500 | 4.6047 | 1.4409 | 2.4995 | 4.0206 | 2.8817 | 2.6344 | | | |
| 8. | 9.8042 | .9500 | 4.7688 | 1.2966 | 2.9170 | 3.7263 | 4.8233 | 2.6861 | 2.1130 | | |
| 9. | 11.300 | 1.0500 | 4.6967 | 1.5118 | 2.8842 | 5.0077 | 4.9432 | 5.3276 | 2.3760 | 1.6391 | |
| 10. | 12.804 | .9500 | 4.8146 | 1.3577 | 3.1682 | 4.5461 | 6.3773 | 5.0336 | 4.6322 | 1.6938 | 1.0401 |

In terms of $c_k$, the residue at any pole of the delay function must be $-1/\sqrt{1 - c_k^2}$ (from Eq. 3-68). Therefore, for any given value of $\epsilon$, simultaneous equations of the following form are generated:

$$1 - \frac{2\epsilon c_k^2}{(1 - c_k^2)^{3/2}} \frac{q}{\pi} \sum_{i \neq k}^{q} \frac{c_k + c_i}{c_k - c_i} = 0 \quad k = 1, 2, \ldots q$$

(3-84)

These equations may be solved simultaneously on a digital computer.† Note, however, that the nominal value of the delay does not enter Eq. 3-84, but only the error $\epsilon$. What determines $\tau$? What is the per cent delay error?

The coefficients of the corresponding all-pole equi-ripple delay function are given in Table 3.1 [B2.427], based on a nominal delay of 1 second [Fig. 3-6] (see [B1.107] for scaling). Since the equi-ripple is a more efficient approximation then the maximally flat, we can expect $\omega_c$ to be greater for the same allowable delay variation. We note, for example, that when a delay error of $\pm 1\%$ is permitted from $\omega = 0$ to $\omega = 6$, an eighth degree, maximally flat, approximating function is necessary, whereas only a sixth degree equi-ripple function is required.

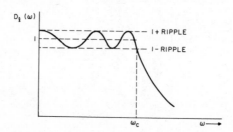

Fig. 3-6. Normalized delay for Table 3.1.

## 3.4. Realization of Elliptic Magnitude Response

Although it is not within the scope of this text to discuss realization techniques at length, the inclusion of some discussion should enable the reader to use the literature available on elliptic filters.

---

† Existence and uniqueness of solution have not been shown; however, the solutions given in Table 3.1 are usually considered to be the only solutions.

1. Since all the zeros of $T(s)$ of Eq. 3-8 are on the imaginary axis, one immediately considers using zero-shifting, pole-removal realization techniques, thus yielding singly-terminated ladders in the form of Fig. 3-7.

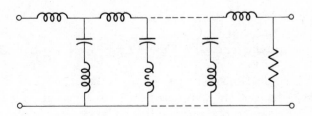

**Fig. 3-7. Singly-terminated ladder.**

2. If it is desired to realize $T(s)$ as the insertion loss of a doubly-terminated network (Fig. 3-8), then $|T(j\infty)|$† $= 0$ since all L's and C's must become open or short circuits as $\omega \rightarrow \infty$.

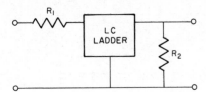

**Fig. 3-8. Doubly-terminated ladder.**

But only a $T(s)$ formed from odd-order elliptic functions fulfills this requirement; hence certain frequency transformations [B2.716] are used to obtain a zero at infinity when n is even.

3. In developing doubly-terminated ladders, transmission zeros must be realized in a specified order [B2.709, 2.717]. Also, the calculations involved require great accuracy [B2.215, 2.727] to insure a reasonable response. This being the case, tables of element values for elliptic filters have been prepared [B2.724, 2.732]. In the latter, the filters are described by the notation (for example)

---

† The other possibility (that $|T(j\infty)| \rightarrow \dfrac{R_1}{R_1 + R_2}$) is uninteresting for typical values of $R_1$ and $R_2$. By similar reasoning, it is clear that $|T(jo)| = R_1/(R_1 + R_2)$.

C        04      30      45           b

Cauer    4th order    $\alpha$    $\sin^{-1} m^{1/2}$    type of frequency transformation

where

$$\text{Passband tolerance (db)} = 10 \log \left[ 1 - \left(\frac{\alpha}{100}\right)^2 \right] \quad (3\text{-}85)$$

4. It is possible to obtain more than one bandpass network realization from the same low-pass realization. Thus, beginning with the even order elliptic filter realization of Fig. 3-9a, we may, by the standard

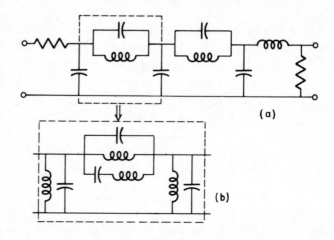

(a)

(b)

**Fig. 3-9.** Single-element frequency transformation.

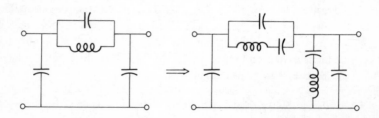

**Fig. 3-10.** Minimum-inductance frequency transformation.

transformation of each L and C, obtain the bandpass network section of Fig. 3-9b. On the other hand, we can allow more freedom in the form of the final network by transforming entire sections (rather than single elements) of the filter at a time. Thus, we can transform a section into the alternative form of Fig. 3-10, while realizing the same overall transfer function as with the standard single-element transformation (although it requires a different resistive termination). The network of Fig. 3-10, for example, has the practical advantage of containing the fewest number of inductors possible† [B2.717, 2.210, 2.321]. The section transformation shown in Fig. 3-11 [B2.717], on the other hand, allows all inductors to contain parasitic stray capacitances.

5. The use of predistortion to correct for losses in low-pass filters is given in [B2.211, 2.713, 2.714, 2.720, 2.722, 2.728, 2.730, 2.731].

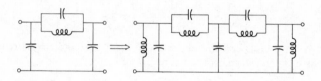

**Fig. 3-11.** Parasitic capacitance transformation.

## PROBLEMS

**3.1.** Use the function found in Problem 2.6 together with Eq. 3-1 to obtain the low-pass characteristic of Fig. 3-1.

**3.2.** Plot the numerator of the solution of Problem 2.6 together with a fourth order Tchebycheff polynomial with unity leading coefficient. Do

---

† It is also interesting to note that the basic circuit element in the latter is an equivalent circuit of a crystal.

64    MODERN NETWORK SYNTHESIS: APPROXIMATION

you see any network theory application by using the polynomial to generate an all-pole function? If so, state precisely.

3.3. Does any other all-pole transfer function have as many ripples in its magnitude response as the Tchebycheff of the same degree? Defend.

3.4. The rationality requirement (for elliptic magnitude response)

$$N = \frac{K(m'_1) K(m)}{K(m_1) K(m')}$$

is apparently violated when we force N to be an integer in step 2 of the design procedure. How do you explain this apparent discrepancy?

3.5. To obtain a double bandpass characteristic, Watanabe [B2.323] sugguested that we let

$$|T(j\omega)|^2 = \frac{1}{1 \pm \epsilon F(\omega)}$$

where $F(\omega)$ satisfies the differential equation

$$\left(\frac{dF}{d\omega}\right)^2 - \frac{k(1 - F^2)}{(1 - \omega^2)\left[1 - \left(\frac{\omega}{\omega_0}\right)^2\right]} L(\omega) = 0$$

Assuming $L(\omega)$ contains only the poles of $F(\omega)$, under what conditions can $F(\omega)$ be written in the closed form

$$F(\omega) = \cos 2 \cos^{-1} \sqrt{\frac{A(\omega)}{B(\omega)}}$$

where $A(\omega)$, $B(\omega)$ are polynomials? Note that $F(\omega)$ is then a rational function.

3.6. Solve (as far as possible) the equi-ripple delay program for the bandpass case [B2.423], given band edges $\omega_1$ and $\omega_2$.

3.7. We wish to point out some possibilities for the use of elliptic functions in the approximation of magnitude responses by network functions with poles on the negative real axis (and, hence, RC realizable) [B2.307]. The three cases we consider are shown in Fig. 3-12 (a-c).

All of these approximating functions can be formed from equations of the type

$$|T(j\omega)|^2 = \frac{1}{1 \pm F(\omega^2)}$$

where the pole-zero configurations of $F(\omega^2)$ are shown for each case in Fig. 3-12 (d-f), respectively (all poles and zeros of $F(\omega)$ are double).

(a) Find $F(\omega^2)$ for the RC low-pass case of Fig. 3-12a.
(b) Show the s-plane pole-zero locations.
(c) Derive the associated design formulae.

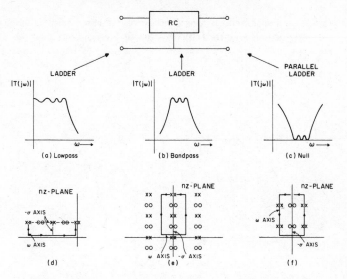

**Fig. 3-12.** Realization of equi-ripple responses with RC networks.

(d) Show, in contrast to the RLC realizable elliptic approximating functions where *any* cutoff rate can be achieved if N is sufficiently large, that now the rate is constrained by the RC-realizable requirement.

(e) Repeat a-d for the response of Fig. 3-12b.

(f) Repeat a-d for the response of Fig. 3-12c.

**3.8.** It is desired to obtain a $v_2(t)$ and $v_3(t)$ (Fig. 3-13) such that $v_2(t) = \sin(\omega t + \theta(\omega))$ and $v_3(t) = \sin(\omega t + \theta(\omega) + 90° \pm \delta)$ when $\delta \leqslant \delta_0$; i.e., $v_1(t)$ and $v_3(t)$ are of the same magnitude and differ in phase by approximately 90°. Show how T(s) of Example 3.2 could be used in obtaining $t_{12}(s)$ and $t_{13}(s)$. See [B2.415] for realizations.

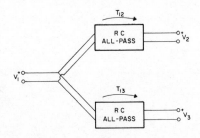

**Fig. 3-13.** A model for realization of constant phase difference.

**3.9.** (a) Show that N, which foretells the network complexity, is given (approximately) as in Table 3.2 for the respective filters [B1.101].

### TABLE 3.2

| Filter | N |
|---|---|
| Butterworth | $B_0 \ln \dfrac{\epsilon_2}{\epsilon_1}$ |
| Tchebycheff | $\left(\dfrac{B_0}{2}\right)^{1/2} \ln \dfrac{2\epsilon_2}{\epsilon_1}$ |
| Elliptic | $\dfrac{2}{\pi^2} \ln \dfrac{4\epsilon_2}{\epsilon_1} \ln 8B_0$ |

$$B_0 = \frac{1}{\omega_0 - 1}$$

(b) How much predistortion can be allowed in the *poles* of the transfer functions of the above (in terms of the specifications)?

# 4

# FREQUENCY TRANSFORMATIONS

In contrast to the usual problem of transforming only a magnitude characteristic from low to a passband [B1.107], we consider, consistent with previous interests (Chapter 1), the problem of simultaneous transformation of magnitude and delay characteristics.

## 4.1. Magnitude

Given a function $T(s)$ with a certain magnitude characteristic for $s = j\omega$, the standard low to bandpass transformation is

$$\omega = \frac{\omega_1\omega_2}{\omega_2 - \omega_1}\left(\frac{\bar{\omega}}{\omega_1\omega_2} - \frac{\omega_1\omega_2}{\omega}\right) \qquad (4\text{-}1)$$

$$= \omega\,(\bar{\omega}) \qquad (4\text{-}2)$$

so that we may form Table. 4.1.

**TABLE 4.1**

| $\omega$ | $\bar{\omega}$ |
|---|---|
| $-1$ | $\omega_1, \; -\omega_2$ |
| $0$ | $\pm\,\omega_1\,\omega_2$ |
| $1$ | $\omega_2, \; -\omega_1$ |

67

If we define

$$\bar{T}(j\bar{\omega}) = T[j\omega\,(\bar{\omega})] \qquad (4\text{-}3)$$

it follows that

$$|\bar{T}(j\bar{\omega})| = |T(j\omega)|_{\omega\,=\,\omega(\bar{\omega})} \qquad (4\text{-}4)$$

Therefore, we may write, in summary

$$|\bar{T}(j\bar{\omega})|_{\omega_1 \leq \bar{\omega} \leq \omega_2} = |\bar{T}(j\bar{\omega})|_{-\omega_1 \leq \bar{\omega} \leq \omega_2} = |T[j\omega(\bar{\omega})]|_{-1 \leq \omega \leq +1} \qquad (4\text{-}5)$$

i.e., for every $-1 \leq \omega \leq +1$ there exists an $-\omega_1 \leq \bar{\omega} \leq -\omega_2$ and $\omega_1 \leq \bar{\omega} \leq \omega_2$ such that Eq. 4-3 is satisfied (although the frequency scale is distorted in the transformation [Fig. 4-16]).

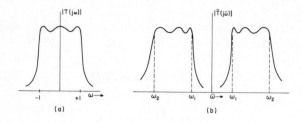

**Fig. 4-1.** Standard low-to-midband magnitude transformation.

When such a transformation is made, it is well to note the effect on the delay characteristic. We therefore define

$$\bar{D}_f(\bar{\omega}) = \frac{-d\,\arg\,\bar{T}(j\bar{\omega})}{d\bar{\omega}} \qquad (4\text{-}6)$$

$$D_f(\omega) = \frac{-d\,\arg\,T(j\omega)}{d\omega} \qquad (4\text{-}7)$$

$$\bar{D}_f(\bar{\omega}) = \frac{-d\,\arg\,T[j\omega(\bar{\omega})]}{d\bar{\omega}} \qquad (4\text{-}8)$$

$$= \left[\frac{-d\,\arg\,T(j\omega)}{d\omega}\right]\left(\frac{d\omega}{d\bar{\omega}}\right)\Bigg|_{\omega\,=\,\omega(\bar{\omega})} \qquad (4\text{-}9)$$

$$= [D_f(\omega)] \bigg|_{\omega = \omega(\bar{\omega})} \left[ \frac{\omega_1\omega_2}{\omega_2 - \omega_1} \left( \frac{1}{\omega_1\omega_2} + \frac{\omega_1\omega_2}{\bar{\omega}^2} \right) \right]$$

(4-10)

transformed low-           distortion
pass delay
characteristic

Thus, comparing Eqs. 4-4 and 4-10, we see that when a low-pass transfer function (with, for example, maximally flat delay) is transformed by means of Eq. 4-1, the resultant delay of the bandpass function $T(j\bar{\omega})$ is distorted (no longer maximally flat).

## 4.2. Delay

We may similarly propose a transformation which preserves delay but at a cost to the magnitude characteristic [B2.423, 2.429].

Given a $T(s)$ with a certain delay characteristic for $s = j\omega$, consider the transformations

$$\omega_\pm = \frac{2\bar{\omega} \pm (\omega_1 + \omega_2)}{\omega_2 - \omega_1}$$

(4-11)

$$= \omega_\pm(\bar{\omega})$$

(4-12)

which is a combination of shifting and scaling of $\omega$ (Table 4.2).

**TABLE 4.2**

| $\omega$ | $\bar{\omega}$ |
|---|---|
| $-1$ | $-\omega_2,\ \omega_1$ |
| $0$ | $\pm(\omega_2 + \omega_1)/2$ |
| $+1$ | $-\omega_1,\ \omega_2$ |

We now define

$$T(j\bar{\omega}) = T[j\omega(\bar{\omega})_+]\ \ T[j\omega(\bar{\omega})_-]$$

(4-13)

then

$$D_\ell(\bar\omega) = \frac{-d\{arg\ T[j\omega(\bar\omega)_+] + arg\ T[j\omega(\bar\omega)_-]\}}{d\bar\omega}$$

(4-14)

$$= -\left\{\left[\frac{d\ arg\ T(j\omega)}{d\omega}\right]\left[\frac{2}{\omega_2 - \omega_1}\right]\right\}\bigg|_{\omega\,=\,\omega(\bar\omega)\,+}$$

$$-\left\{\left[d\ \frac{arg\ T(j\omega)}{j\omega}\right]\left[\frac{2}{\omega_2 - \omega_1}\right]\right\}\bigg|_{\omega\,=\,\omega(\bar\omega)\,-}$$

(4-15)

$$= \left[\frac{2}{\omega_2 - \omega_1}\right]\left[D_\ell(\omega)\big|_{\omega\,=\,\omega(\bar\omega)\,+}\right.$$

$$+ D_\ell(\omega)\big|_{\omega\,=\,\omega(\bar\omega)\,-}\bigg]$$

(4-16)

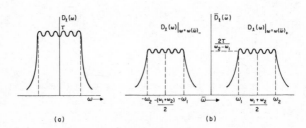

**Fig. 4-2. Low-to-midband delay transformation.**

Since $D_\ell(\omega)\big|_{\omega\to\infty} \to 0$ (Eq. 1-33), if the shift of the delay characteristic by $\pm\ (\omega_2+\omega_1)/2$ (Eq. 4-11) is sufficiently large, then the components of $\bar D_\ell(\bar\omega)$ (Eq. 4-16 and Fig. 4-2) do not affect each other; hence,

$$\bar D_\ell(\bar\omega) \approx \left(\frac{2}{\omega_2 - \omega_1}\right)D_\ell(\omega)\ \bigg|_{\omega\,=\,\omega(\bar\omega)\,+}\quad \omega_1 \leqslant \bar\omega \leqslant \omega_2$$

(4-17)

$$D_f(\bar{\omega}) \approx \left(\frac{2}{\omega_2 - \omega_1}\right) D_f(\omega) \Bigg|_{\omega = \omega(\bar{\omega}) -} \qquad -\omega_2 \leqslant \omega \leqslant -\omega_1$$

$$(4\text{-}18)$$

Thus, if $D_f(\omega)$ is maximally flat at $\omega = 0$, $D_f(\bar{\omega})$ is nearly maximally flat at $\omega = \pm \; (\omega_1 + \omega_2)/2$. The effect on the transformed magnitude characteristic is studied in Problem 4.1.

## PROBLEMS

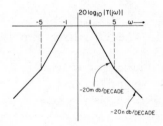

**Fig. 4-3. Magnitude specification (Problem 4.1).**

**4.1.** Assuming that $20 \log |T(j\omega)|$ may be approximated as in Fig. 4-3:

(a) Show the resultant magnitude characteristic $|\bar{T}(j\bar{\omega})|$ when defined as in Eq. 4-13 (assuming $\omega_1 = 15$, $\omega_2 = 16$) for (1) $m = n = 2$, and (2) $m = 3$, $n = 2$.

(b) Comment on the relative merits of the transformations in Eqs. 4-1 and 4-11.

(c) Suppose we define the transformation

$$\bar{T}(j\omega) = j\omega^n T[j\omega(\bar{\omega})_+] \; T \; [j\omega(\bar{\omega})_-] \qquad (4\text{-}19)$$

1. What is the effect of $s^n$ on the delay given in Eq. 4-16?
2. What is the effect of $s^n$ on the bandpass magnitude characteristic as given in (a)?
3. Compare this transformation with that of Eq. 4-1 when $T(s)$ is an all-pole function.

# 5

# USE OF THE COMPUTER IN APPROXIMATION

## 5.1. The Equalizer Problem

The approximation problems considered up to this point have one common objective: the approximation of a *constant* over a range of frequencies. The more general problem, however, is the approximation of an arbitrary (but well-behaved) magnitude, phase, or delay characteristic. For example, such a problem could arise when attempting to "equalize" the magnitude characteristic of a physical device (from cables to crystal cartridges), or, from the discussion in Section 1.2, when equalizing the delay characteristic of a Tchebycheff response function to achieve a nearly constant magnitude and delay simultaneously (Fig. 5-1) [B2.209, 2.213].

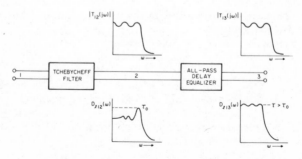

**Fig. 5-1.** Typical delay equalization scheme.

72

A simple but practical two-step procedure to accomplish equalization in the general case is the following:

1. Obtain a rough approximation to the desired magnitude, phase, or delay curve by break-point synthesis.
2. Improve the approximation by means of an iterative computer technique.

Since knowledge of (1) is assumed [B1.107], we will discuss only (2).

## 5.2. Computer Refinement

Suppose that it is desired to approximate (for convenience, in the least square error sense) a desired magnitude† specification $|T_s(j\omega)|$ (specified at values $\omega = \omega_1, \ldots, \omega_k$) by a function of the form

$$T(s) = \frac{\displaystyle\sum_i^p a_i \, s^i}{\displaystyle\sum_j^q a_{p+j} \, s^j} \tag{5-1}$$

where p and q are given. The mean square error is then

$$ERR = \frac{1}{k} \sum_r^k [|T(j\omega_r)| - |T_s(j\omega_r)|]^2 \tag{5-2}$$

If we now change $a_i$ to $a_i + \Delta a_i$ in an effort to decrease the error, we find

$$ERR_\Delta - ERR = \Delta \, ERR \tag{5-3}$$

$$\approx \frac{d \, ERR}{d \, a_i} \times \Delta \, a_i \tag{5-4}$$

so that $\Delta$ ERR will be negative if the chosen sign of $\Delta \, a_i$ is opposite to that of d ERR/d $a_i$.

When more than one coefficient is being varied, we may define a gradient vector .

---

† The same analysis will apply to delay and phase equalization.

$$\widehat{G} = \sum \frac{\partial \text{ ERR}}{\partial a_i} \widehat{a_i} \qquad (5\text{-}5)$$

and the vector

$$\widehat{\Delta a} = \sum \Delta a_i \widehat{a_i} \qquad (5\text{-}6)$$

so that the scalar product of G and $\Delta$ a is

$$(\widehat{G}, \widehat{\Delta a}) = \sum \frac{\partial \text{ ERR}}{\partial a_i} \widehat{\Delta a_i} \qquad (5\text{-}7)$$

$$\approx \Delta \text{ ERR} \qquad (5\text{-}8)$$

If we restrict the length of $\widehat{\Delta a}$ to a given $\Delta$ a (called the step size), i.e.,

$$\Delta a = \sqrt{\Sigma \Delta a_i^2} \qquad (5\text{-}9)$$

then the scalar product of Eq. 5-7 is minimized when $\widehat{\Delta a}$ and $\widehat{G}$ are co-linear, i.e.,

$$\Delta a_i + - \alpha \frac{\partial \text{ ERR}}{\partial a_i} \qquad (5\text{-}10)$$

To satisfy Eq. 5-9, we choose $\alpha$ to be

$$\alpha = \frac{\Delta \text{ a}}{\sqrt{\Sigma \left( \frac{\partial \text{ ERR}}{\partial a_i} \right)^2}} \qquad (5\text{-}11)$$

so that

$$\sqrt{\Sigma \Delta a_i^2} = \sqrt{\alpha^2 \sum \left( \frac{\partial \text{ ERR}}{\partial a_i} \right)^2} \qquad (5\text{-}12)$$

$$= \Delta a \qquad (5\text{-}13)$$

Hence, the desired change is

$$\Delta a_i = \frac{-\Delta \text{ a} \left( \frac{\partial \text{ ERR}}{\partial a_i} \right)}{\sqrt{\Sigma \left( \frac{\partial \text{ ERR}}{\partial a_i} \right)^2}} \qquad (5\text{-}14)$$

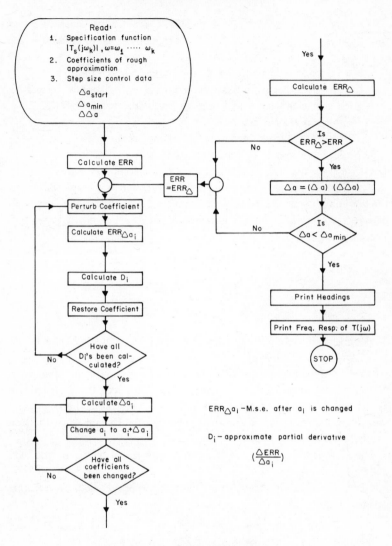

**Fig. 5-2.** Computer flow chart.

which will minimize the $\Delta$ERR. This technique for changing the $a_i$ is known as the method of steepest descent.[†]

_____

[†] Any scheme which proceeds in the direction of the gradient is so called. The selection of the step size $\Delta a$ (equally important) may vary according to the problem [B2.202, 2.211].

We may devise, from Eqs. 5-2 and 5-14, iterative schemes that will successively alter the original transfer function so as to minimize the error of Eq. 5-2:

1. Choose a $\Delta a$ sufficiently small so that Eq. 5-4 is valid.
2. Calculate the partial derivatives $\partial$ ERR$/\partial$ $a_i$ by slightly perturbing each coefficient and calculating the resultant change in ERR.
3. Calculate $\Delta$ $a_i$ as in Eq. 5-14.
4. Permanently change each $a_i$ by an amount $\Delta$ $a_i$.
5. Repeat the process by returning to (1).

These steps are readily programmed on a digital computer.

Note that no property of the magnitude function was employed in the foregoing argument. As long as the function being approximated is well-behaved (so that a Taylor's series exists at each $\omega_k$), a small enough step size can be chosen so that Eq. 5-4 is a good approximation. Thus, the same technique can be used to approximate rather arbitrary phase and delay characteristics.

## 5.3. A Sample Program†

Having an initial approximating function T(s) obtained from break-point synthesis, and having some estimate of the step size ($\Delta$ a) to be taken, we may construct a simple flow chart for the iteration (Fig. 5-2). Note that we must have a provision ($\Delta\Delta a$) to decrease the step size as the process converges (so that we do not "overshoot" the true minimum) and that we must also provide to stop the program when the step size becomes small ($\Delta a_{min}$).

The complete program (in Fortran language) is given in the Appendix.†

When a magnitude characteristic is being approximated, the error is calculated from

$$\text{ERR} = \frac{1}{k} \sum_{r}^{k} [20 \log_{10} |T_s(j\omega_r)| - 20 \log_{10} |T(j\omega_r)|]^2$$

$$(5\text{-}15)$$

---

† The reader is referred to the problems for further uses of the steepest descent method.

† This program is not in any sense optimum, but is simple and has been found to converge from rather poor initial guesses.

so that the curve will be approximated equally well on a logarithmic basis over its entire range.

*Example 5.1:* We desire to approximate the data given in Table 5.1 with a rational function of order no higher than 5.

## TABLE 5.1

| RADIAN FREQUENCY | MAGNITUDE (DB) | RADIAN FREQUENCY | MAGNITUDE (DB) |
|---|---|---|---|
| 1 | 20 | 50 | −4.2 |
| 2 | 14 | 70 | −6.5 |
| 4 | 8.5 | 100 | −9.5 |
| 8 | 4 | 150 | −13.8 |
| 10 | 2.8 | 200 | −17.0 |
| 15 | 0.8 | 300 | −22.5 |
| 30 | −1.8 | 500 | −40.0 |
| 40 | −3.0 | 1000 | −61.5 |

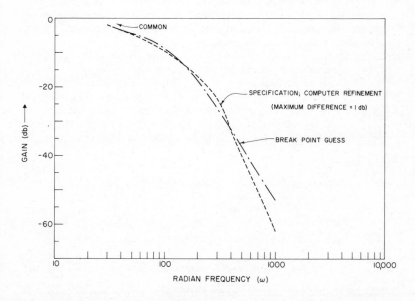

**Fig. 5-3.** Computer improvement of break point analysis (example).

Using only first order approximation terms, we decide to choose

$$T(s) = \frac{100(s + 10)(s + 560)(s + 600)}{(s + .1)(s + 40)(s + 200)(s + 360)(s + 370)}$$

$$\Delta a_{start} = .1 \quad \Delta a_{min} = .01 \quad \Delta \Delta a = .5$$

The quantity $|T(j\omega)|$ is plotted (Fig. 5-3) together with the resultant computer refinement.[†] The error (as measured in Eq. 5-15 at the data points) is decreased from .88 to .113 and the maximum deviation of the refinement from the specification is 1 db. The execution time was 1 minute on an IBM 7090.

## PROBLEMS

5.1. It has been suggested that, rather than successively changing the *coefficients* of an initial approximating function $T(s)$, we obtain a network realization of $T(s)$ and then, in turn, change the *element values* to achieve the desired convergence.

    (a) Comment on the advantages and disadvantages of this alternative approach, particularly for two-element kind networks.

    (b) Consider the application of this technique to ladder networks:

        1. Draw the flow chart of a subroutine to calculate $|t_{21}(j\omega_k)|$ of the ladder of Fig. 5-4 (given the element values and $\omega_k$).

        2. Draw the flow chart of the complete computer program (using the steepest descent method) which will iteratively change the

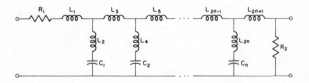

**Fig. 5-4.** A low-pass doubly-terminated ladder model.

---

[†] The refinement has complex poles to achieve the required cutoff (see Problem 1a).

element values of Fig. 5-4 to approximate a general magnitude characteristic.

   3. Discuss (a) further for the ladder.
   4. Write the Fortran program.
(c). Extend (b) to non-uniformly lossy ladders [B2.211].

5.2. How could the program of Problem 5.1 be used to detect the amount elements in a physical network differ from their ideal values?

5.3. The sample program is written purposely inefficient for clarity. Find as many inefficiencies as possible, employing the steepest descent method.

5.4. It is desired to devise a method for computing element values of "near elliptic" filters of high degree (greater than available in tables) with arbitrary passband and stopband tolerances. The following method is suggested (for odd order filters, where no frequency transformation is required):

(a) From $\epsilon_1$ and $\epsilon_2$, compute m, m', and N. Then re-calculate the $\epsilon_2$ actually realized when an integer value for N is used.

(b) Compute the frequencies of stopband and passband minima and maxima, partially from formulae of Chapter 3.

(c) From an initial guess of topology and element values (which realize exactly the transmission zeros calculated in (b)), change the element values as in Problem 5.1 while realizing the exact transmission zeros at each step.

In implementing the above, one must solve the following problems:

   1. Derive the formulae for determining the quantities of parts (a) and (b).
   2. How would you make an initial guess of the element values?
   3. From (a) and (b), devise an error criterion which will allow convergence of the element values to values yielding a "near-elliptic" response.
   4. Assuming the network topology is that given in Fig. 5-4, write a subroutine which will calculate

$$|t(j\omega_k)|_{k=1,\,2}$$

given $L_{2n-1}$ (n = 1, 2, ...), $C_n$, $z_n$ (the transmission zero), and $\omega_k$. Note that $L_{2r}$ is determined by $C_r$ and $z_r$ and that the transmission zeros must be realized in a certain order (Section 3.5).

Although no strict claim for convergence can be made, it has been found possible to converge from some rather poor initial guesses. Indeed, when only one high degree filter is desired, this method is very useful since there is no accuracy problem and a Fortran program may be readily written.

5.5. Why is $\tau > \tau_0$ in Fig. 5-1?

**APPENDICES**

# Appendix I

## SAMPLE CONVERGING RESPONSE †

(Magnitude, Phase, or Delay; JA = 2, 3, 4)

NA—Number of Numerator Coefficients
NB—Number of Denominator Coefficients
NI—Number of Data Points
JA—Input Selector
DELA—Initial Step Size
DELMIN—Minimum Step Size
DELDEL—Change in Step Size
A(I, 1)—Initial Numerator Coefficients
B(I, 1)—Initial Denominator Coefficients
OMEGA(J)—Data Points
FCTN(J)—Desired Data Values

```
    DIMENSION A(30,2), B(30,2), G(4), D(60), SUMSQ(2),
            DLY(2), OMEGA(100), FCTN(100)
 24 READ INPUT TAPE 7, 1, NA, NB, NI, JA, DELA, DELMIN,
            DELDEL
  1 FORMAT (4(I2, 1X)/(F10.0))
    READ INPUT TAPE 7, 2, (A(I, 1), I = 1, NA), (B(J, 1), J = 1,
            NB), (OMEGA (J), J = 1, NI), (FCTN(J), J = 1, NI)
  2 FORMAT (8F10.0)
    DLY(1) = 0.0
    C = NI
 25 LL = 1
    DO 26 J = 1, NA
 26 A(J, 2) = A(J, 1)
    DO 27 J = 1, NB
 27 B(J, 2) = B(J, 1)
    SUMSQ(LL) = 0.0
  3 DO 4 K = 1, NI
    W = OMEGA (K)
    CALL FREQ (NA, NB, A, B, G, W)
  4 SUMSQ(LL) = SUMSQ(LL) + (G(JA) − FCTN(K)) **2
    SUMSQ(LL) = SUMSQ(LL)/C
```

† Written, in part, by D. S. Humphreys.

```
      GO TO (13, 14, 15), LL
 16   LL = 2
      SQMIN = 0.0
      DO 5 KA = 1, NA
      IF (KA−1) 6, 6, 7
  7   A(KA−1, 2) = A(KA−1, 1)
  6   A(KA, 2) = A(KA, 1) ★ (1.0 + DELA)
      GO TO 3
 14   D(KA) = SUMSQ (2) − SUMSQ(1)
  5   SQMIN = SQMIN + (D (KA)) ★★2
      A(NA, 2) = A(NA, 1)
      LL = 3
      DO 8 KB = 1, NB
      IF(KB−1) 9, 9, 10
 10   B(KB−1, 2) = B(KB−1, 1)
  9   B(KB, 2) = B(KB, 1) ★ (1.0 + DELA)
      GO TO 3
 15   KBB = KB + NA
      D(KBB) = SUMSQ (3) − SUMSQ(1)
  8   SQMIN = SQMIN + (D (KBB)) ★★2
      B(NB, 2) = B(NB, 1)
      SRT = SQRT (SQMIN)
      DO 11 K = 1, NA
 11   A(K, 1) = A(K, 1) ★ (1.0 − DELA ★ D(K)/SRT)
      DO 12 K = 1, NB
      KBB = K + NA
 12   B(K, 1) = B(K, 1) ★ (1.0 − DELA ★ D(KBB)/SRT)
      GO TO 25
 13   DLY(2) = DLY(1)
      DLY(1) = SUMSQ(1)
      IF (DLY(2)) 17, 16, 17
 17   IF (DLY(2) − DLY(1)) 18, 18, 16
 18   DELA = DELDEL ★ DELA
      IF (DELA−DELMIN) 20, 16, 16
 20   DO 28 J = 1, NA
 28   A(J, 2) = A(J, 1)
      DO 29 J = 1, NB
 29   B(J, 2) = B(J, 1)
      WRITE OUTPUT TAPE 6, 21
 21   FORMAT (12X, 5HOMEGA, 8X, 9HAMPL (DB), 5X,
              5HPHASE, 8X, 5HDELAY)
      DO 22 J = 1, NI
      W = OMEGA (J)
```

```
      CALL FREQ (NA, NB, A, B, G, W)
      WRITE OUTPUT TAPE 6, 23, (G(I), I = 1, 4)
   23 FORMAT (E20.6, E15.6, F10.3, E15.6)
      CONTINUE
      GO TO 24
      END


      SUBROUTINE FREQ (NA, NB, A, B, G, W)
      DIMENSION A(30, 2), B(30, 2), AE(15), AO(15), AE1(15),
      AO1(15), BE(15), BO(15), BE1(15), BO1(15), G(4)
      CALL PARTS (NA, A, M1, AE, N1, AO, M11, AE1, N11, AO1)
      CALL PARTS (NB, B, M2, BE, N2, BO, M12, BE1, N12, BO1)
      EVN = SUM (M1, AE, W)
      ODD N = W * SUM (N1, AO, W)
      EVIN = W * SUM (M11, AE1, W)
      ODDIN = SUM (N11, AO1, W)
      EVD = SUM (M2, BE, W)
      ODDD = W * SUM (N2, BO, W)
      EVID = W * SUM (M12, BE1, W)
      ODDID = SUM (N12, BO1, W)
      TOP = EVN * EVN + ODDN * ODDN
      BOTTOM = EVD * EVD + ODDD * ODDD
      Y = ODDN * EVD - ODDD * EVN
      X = EVN * EVD + ODDD * ODDN
      G(1) = W
      G(2) = 4.3429448 * LOG (G(2))
      G(3) = 57.2957795 * ATAN(Y, X)
      G(4) = (EVD * ODDID + ODDD * EVID)/BOTTOM -
             (EVN * ODDIN + ODDN * EVIN)/TOP
      RETURN
      END


      SUBROUTINE PARTS (NA, A, MK, AE, NK, AO, MIK, AE1,
            N1K, AO1)
      DIMENSION A(30, 2), AE(15), AO(15), AE1(15), AO1(15)
      I = 1
      MK = 1
      NK = 0
      MIK = 0
      AE(1) = A(1, 2)
      IF (NA-I) 3, 3, 1
    1 I = I + 1
      NK = NK + 1
```

```
      AO(NR) = A(I, 2)
      DUMMY = I − 1
      AO1(NK) = DUMMY ⋆ A(I, 2)
      IF (NA−I) 3, 3, 2
    2 MIK = MK
      MK = MK + 1
      I = I + 1
      AE(MK) = A(I, 2)
      DUMMY = I − 1
      AE1(MIK) = DUMMY ⋆ A(I, 2)
      IF (NA−I) 3, 3, 1
    3 N1K = NK
      RETURN
      END

      FUNCTION SUM (N, A, W)
      DIMENSION A(30, 2)
      SUM = 0.0
      IF (N) 3, 3, 2
    2 SUM = A (N, 2)
      IF (N−1) 3, 3, 4
    4 X = −W ⋆ W
      NM1 = N−1
      DO 5 I = 1, NM1
      K = N−I
    5 SUM = SUM ⋆ X + A(K, 2)
    3 RETURN
      END
```

# Appendix II

## BIBLIOGRAPHY

(Entries preceded by asterisks have been referred to in the text. Titles in each section are listed in chronological order, from the earliest to the latest publication.)

### B1 GENERAL REFERENCE

#### B1.1 *Synthesis Books*

*1.101 Storer, J. E., *Passive Network Synthesis*. New York, N.Y.: McGraw-Hill Book Company, Inc., 1957.

*1.102 Guillemin, E. A., *Synthesis of Passive Networks*. New York, N.Y.: John Wiley & Sons, Inc., 1957.

1.103 Balbanian, N., *Network Synthesis*. Englewood Cliffs, N.J.: Prentice-Hall, Inc., 1958.

1.104 Cauer, W., *Synthesis of Linear Communication Networks*. New York, N.Y.: McGraw-Hill Book Company, Inc., 1958.

*1.105 Tuttle, S., *Network Synthesis*. New York, N.Y.: John Wiley & Sons, Inc., 1958.

1.106 Kuh, E. S. and D. O. Pederson, *Principles of Circuit Synthesis*. New York, N.Y.: McGraw-Hill Book Company, Inc., 1959.

*1.107 Van Valkenburg, M. E., *Introduction to Modern Network Synthesis*. New York, N.Y.: John Wiley & Sons, Inc., 1960.

*1.108 Weinberg, L., *Network Analysis and Synthesis*. New York, N.Y.: McGraw-Hill Book Company, Inc., 1962.

1.109 Kuo, F. E., *Network Analysis and Synthesis*. New York, N.Y.: John Wiley & Sons, Inc., 1962.

1.110 Hazony, D., *Elements of Network Synthesis*. New York, N.Y.: Reinhold Publishing Corp., 1963.

#### B1.2 *Other Books*

1.201 Bode, H. W., *Network Analysis and Feedback Amplifier Design*. Princeton, N.J.: D. Van Nostrand Company, Inc., 1945.

*1.202 Valley, G. E. and H. Wallman, *Vacuum Tube Amplifiers*. Vol. 18, Rad. Lab. Series, New York, N.Y.: McGraw-Hill Book Company, Inc., 1948.

1.203 Truxal, J. G., *Automatic Feedback Control System Synthesis*. New York, N.Y.: McGraw-Hill Book Company, Inc., 1957.

*1.204  Mason, S. J. and H. J. Zimmerman, *Electronic Circuits, Signals and Systems.* New York, N.Y.: John Wiley & Sons, Inc., 1960.

1.205  De Pian, L., *Linear Active Network Theory.* Englewod Cliffs, N.J.: Prentice-Hall, Inc., 1962.

*1.206  Kim, W. H. and R. T. Chien, *Topological Analysis and Synthesis of Communication Networks.* New York, N.Y.: Columbia University Press, 1962.

1.207  Huelsman, L. P., *Circuits, Matrices, and Linear Vector Spaces.* New York, N.Y.: McGraw-Hill Company, Inc., 1963.

## B2 APPROXIMATION
### (See, also, Reference 2.318)

### B2.1 *General*

2.101  Padé, H., "Sur la Representation Approché d'une Fonction par des Fractions Rationnelles," *Ann. de l'Ecole Normale* (3), Vol. 9, 1892, pp. 1-93.

2.102  Cayley, A., *Elliptic Functions,* 2nd ed. London, England: George Bell & Sons, 1895.

2.103  Bernstein, S., *Leçóns sur les Propriétés Extremales et la Meillure Approximation des Fonctions Analytiques d'une Variable Réelle.* Paris: Verlog Gauthier-Villars, 1926.

2.104  Jackson, D., "The Theory of Approximation," *Amer. Math. Soc. Colloq. Pub.,* Vol. 11, 1930.

2.105  Van der Pol, B. and T. J. Weijers, "Tchebycheff Polynomials and Their Relation to Circular Functions, Bessel Functions and Lissajous Figures," *Physica,* Vol. 1, December, 1933, pp. 78-96.

*2.106  Paley and N. Wiener, "Fourier Transforms in the Complex Domain," *Am. Math. Soc. Colloq. Pub.,* Vol. 19, 1934, pp. 16-17.

2.107  Shohat, J., "Théorie Générale des Polynomes Orthogonaux de Tchebichev," *Mem. des Sci. Math.* (Paris), No. 66, 1934.

2.108  Walsh, J. L., "On Approximation to an Analytic Fuction by Rational Functions of Best Approximation," *Math Zeit.,* Vol. 38, 1931-34, pp. 163-176.

2.109  Bayard, M., "Relations Between the Real and Imaginary Parts of Impedances and Determination of the Function from One of Its Parts," *Rev. Gen. Elec.* (Paris), Vol. 37, May, 1935, pp. 659-664.

2.110  LeCorbeiller, P., "Méthode d'Approximation de Tchebycheff et Application aux Filtres de Fréquences," *Rev. Gen. Elect.* (Paris), Vol. 40, November, 1936, pp. 651-657.

2.111  Leroy, R., "Relationship Between Attenuation and Phase of a Linear Transmission System," *Annales des Postes, Télégraphes et Téléphones,* Vol. 24, August, 1940, pp. 733-740.

*2.112  Spenceley, G. W. and R. M., *Smithsonian Elliptic Function Tables.* Washington, D.C.: Smithsonian Institute, 1947.

2.113 Murakami, T. and M. Corrington, "Relation Between Amplitude and Phase in Electrical Networks," *RCA Rev.,* Vol. 9, December, 1948, pp. 602-631.

*2.114 Milne-Thomson, L. M., *Jacobian Elliptic Function Tables.* New York, N.Y.: Dover Publications, Inc., 1950.

2.115 Klein, W., "Tchebycheff Functions," *Arch. Elektrotech.,* Vol. 39, 1950, pp. 647-657.

2.116 Darlington, S., "Network Synthesis Using Tchebycheff Polynomial Series," *BSTJ,* Vol. 31, July, 1952, pp. 613-665. Also, *Proc. Symposium on Modern Network Synthesis,* April, 1952, pp. 128-139.

2.117 Clement, P. R., "The Chebyshev Approximation Method," *Quart. Appl. Math.,* Vol. 2, July, 1953, pp. 167-183.

2.118 Achieser, N. I., *Theory of Approximation.* New York, N.Y.: Frederick Ungar Publishing Co., Inc., 1956. (Translation of German).

2.119 Pokrovskii, "On a Class of Polynomials with Extremal Properties," *Trans. Amer. Math. Soc.,* Vol. 19, 1962, pp. 199-220.


B2.2 *Computer*

(See *Trans. IRE,* Vol. CT-9, September, 1961; *IRE Conv. Record,* Vol. 10, Part 2, 1962; *Marconi Review,* Vol. 23, 1960.)

2.201 Hastings, C., *Approximation for Digital Computers.* Princeton, N.J.: Princeton University Press, 1955.

*2.202 Aaron, R. M., "The Use of Least Squares in System Design," *Trans. IRE,* Vol. CT-3, December, 1956, pp. 224-231.

2.203 Shenitzer, A., "Chebychev Approximation of a Continuous Function by a Class of Functions," *J. Assoc. Comp. Mach.,* Vol. 4, January, 1957, pp. 30-35.

2.204 Bashkow, T. R. and C. A. Desoer, "Digital Computers and Network Theory," *IRE Wescon Conv. Record,* Part 2, 1957, pp. 133-137.

2.205 Dennis, J. B., *Mathematical Programming and Electrical Networks.* New York, N.Y.: John Wiley & Sons, Inc., 1959.

2.206 Hartl, H., "The Application of Electronic Digital Computers in Network Theory," *Nachricten-Technische,* Vol. 13, No. 7, July, 1960, pp. 313-316.

2.207 Hull, D. J., "Insertion-Loss Equalization with a Digital Computer," *Marconi Rev.,* Vol. 23, 1960, pp. 149-152.

2.208 Temes, G. C., "The Synthesis of General Parameter Insertion Loss Filters Using a Digital Computer," *Trans. AIEE,* Part 1, Comm. and Electronics, Vol. 80, May, 1961, pp. 181-186.

*2.209 Hellerstein, S., "Synthesis of All-Pass Delay Equalizers," *Trans. IRE,* Vol. CT-8, September, 1961, pp. 215-222.

*2.210 Yamamoto, K., K. Fugimoto and H. Watanabe, "Programming the Minimum Inductance Transformation," *Trans. IRE,* Vol. CT-8, September, 1961, pp. 184-191.

*2.211 Desoer, C. A., and S. K. Mitra, "Design of Lossy Ladder Filters by Digital Computer," *Trans. IRE,* Vol. CT-8, September, 1961, pp. 192-201.

2.212 Fall, J. V., "A Digital Computer Program for the Design of Phase Correctors," *Trans. IRE,* Vol. CT-9, September, 1961, pp. 223-236.

*2.213 Semmelman, C. L., "Experience with a Steepest Descent Computer Program for Designing Delay Networks," *IRE Conv. Record,* Vol. 10, Part 2, 1962.

2.214 Temes, G. C., "Filter Synthesis Using a Digital Computer," *IRE Conv. Record,* Vol. 10, Part 2, 1962.

*2.215 Watanabe, H. and others, "A New Calculation Method for the Design of Filters by Digital Computer with the Special Consideration of the Accuracy Problem," *IEEE Conv. Rec.,* Circuit Theory, 1963.

2.216 Fugisawa, T., "Optimization of Low-Pass Attenuation Characteristics by a Digital Computer," *Proc. Sixth Midwest Symp.,* Wisconsin, May, 1963.

## B2.3 *Magnitude*

(See B2.318, also.)

2.301 Butterworth, S., "On the Theory of Filter Amplifiers," *Experimental Wireless,* Vol. 7, October, 1930, pp. 536-541.

2.302 Baum, R. F., "Design of Broadband I. F. Amplifiers," *Jour. Appl. Phys.,* Vol. 17, June, 1946, pp. 519-529; and September, 1946, pp. 721-730.

2.303 Baum, R. F., "A Contribution to the Approximation Problem," *Proc. IRE,* Vol. 36, July, 1948, pp. 863-869.

2.304 Thomson, W. E., "Stagger-Tuned Low-Pass Amplifiers," *Wireless Eng.,* Vol. 26, November, 1949, pp. 357-359.

2.305 Fano, R. M., "A Note on the Solution of Certain Approximation Problems in Network Synthesis," *J. Frank. Inst.,* Vol. 249, March, 1950, pp. 189-205.

2.306 Linke, J. M., "A Graphical Approach to the Synthesis of General Insertion Attenuation Functions," *Proc. IEE,* Vol. 97, Part III, May, 1950, pp. 179-187.

*2.307 Matthaei, G. L., "A General Method for Synthesis of Filter Transfer Functions As Applied to L-C and R-C Filter Examples," *Tech. Rep. No. 39,* Electronic Res. Lab., Stanford Univ., August 31, 1951.

2.308 Matthaei, G. L., "Filter Transfer Function Synthesis," *Proc. IRE.,* Vol. 41, March, 1953, pp. 377-382. Also, *Paper No. 72,* IRE National Convention, New York, N.Y., March, 1952.

2.309 Trautman, D. L., "The Application of Conformal Mapping to the Synthesis of Bandpass Networks," *Modern Network Synthesis,* MRI Symposium Series, April, 1952, pp. 179-192.

2.310 Linvill, J. G., "The Approximation with Rational Functions of Prescribed Magnitude and Phase Characteristics," *Proc. IRE,* Vol. 40, June, 1952, pp. 711-721.

2.311 Saraga, W., "Approximations in Network Design," *Wireless Eng.,* Vol. 29, October, 1952, pp. 280-281.

2.312 Bresler, A. D., "On the Approximation Problem in Network Synthesis," *Proc. IRE,* Vol. 40, December, 1952, pp. 1724-1728.

2.313 Matthaei, G. L., "Filter Transfer Function Synthesis," *Proc. IRE,* Vol. 41, No. 3, March, 1953, pp. 377.

2.314 Atiya, F. S., "Theory of Maximally Flat and Quasi-Tchebycheff Filters," *Arch. Elek. Ubertragung,* Vol. 7, September, 1953, pp. 441-450.

2.315 Matthaei, G. L., "Conformal Mappings for Filter Transfer Function Synthesis," *Proc. IRE,* Vol. 41, November, 1953, pp. 1658-1664.

2.316 Sharpe, C. B., "A General Tchebycheff Rational Function," *Proc. IRE.,* Vol. 42, February, 1954, pp. 454-457.

2.317 Matthaei, G. L., "Some Techniques for Network Synthesis," *Paper No. 39.1,* IRE National Convention, New York, N.Y., March, 1954.

2.318 Winkler, S., "Approximation Problems of Network Synthesis," *Trans. IRE,* Vol. CT-2, No. 3, September, 1954, pp. 5-21.

*2.319 Helman, D., "Tchebycheff Approximations for Amplitude and Delay with Rational Functions," *Modern Network Synthesis,* MRI Symposium Series, Vol. V, 1955, pp. 385-402.

*2.320 Papoulis, A., "On the Approximation Problem in Filter Design," *IRE Conv. Record,* Vol. 5, Part 2, 1957, pp. 175-185.

*2.321 Watanabe, H., "Synthesis of Band-Pass Ladder Network," *Trans. IRE,* Vol. CT-5, December, 1958, pp. 256-264.

2.322 Dishal, J., "Gaussian-Response Filter Design," *Electrical Communications,* Vol. 36, No. 1, 1959, pp. 3-26.

*2.323 Watanabe, H., "Approximation Theory for Filter Networks," *Trans. IRE,* Vol. CT-9, No. 3, September, 1961, pp. 341-356.

2.324 Ku, Y. H. and M. Drubin, "Network Synthesis Using Legendre and Hermite Polynomials," *J. Franklin Inst.,* Vol. 273, No. 2, February, 1962, pp. 138-157.

## B2.4 *Phase and Delay*

(See, also, Section B2.2)

2.401 Thomson, W. E., "Delay Networks Having Maximally Flat Frequency Characteristics," *Proc. IEE* (London), Vol. 96, November, 1949, pp. 487-490.

2.402 Darlington, S., "Realization of a Constant Phase Difference," *BSTJ,* Vol. 29, January, 1950, pp. 94-104.

2.403 Baumann, E., "Impedances with Prescribed Variation of Phase Angle," *Z. Angew, Phys.,* Vol. 1, January 15, 1950, pp. 43-52.

2.404 Orchard, H. J., "Synthesis of Wideband Two-Phase Networks, *Wireless Eng.,* Vol. 27, March, 1950, pp. 72-81.

2.405  Brain, A. E., "The Compensation for Phase Errors in Wide-Band Video Amplifiers," *Proc. IEE,* Part III, Vol. 97, July, 1950, pp. 243-251.

2.406  Saraga, W., "The Design of Wide-Band Phase Splitting Networks," *Proc. IRE,* Vol. 38, July, 1950, pp. 754-770.

2.407  Weaver, D. K., "Constant-Phase-Difference Networks and Their Application to Filters," *Tech. Rep. No. 1,* Electronic Res. Lab., Stanford Univ., October 28, 1950.

2.408  Matthaei, G. L., "Maximally-Flat Phase-Difference Network Design," *Tech. Rep. No. 2,* Electronic Res. Lab., Stanford Univ., October 31, 1950.

2.409  Saraga, W., "Wide-Band Two-Phase Networks," *Wireless Eng.,* Vol. 28, January, 1951, pp. 30-31.

2.410  Orchard, H. J., "Wide-Band Two-Phase Networks," *Wireless Eng.,* Vol. 28, January, 1951, p. 30.

2.411  Thomson, W. E., "Networks with Maximally Flat Delay," *Wireless Eng.,* Vol. 29, October, 1952, pp. 256-263. Correction, Vol. 29, November, 1952, p. 309.

*2.412  Bennett, B. J., "Synthesis of Electric Filters with Arbitrary Phase Characteristics," *IRE Conv. Record,* Part 5, Circuit Theory, March, 1953, pp. 19-26.

2.413  Covington, M. S. and R. W. Sonnenfelot, "Synthesis of Constant Time-Delay Networks," *Proc. NEC,* Vol. 9, September, 1953, pp. 50-63.

2.414  Golay, M., "The Direct Method of Filter and Delay Line Synthesis," *Proc. IRE,* Vol. 42, March, 1954, pp. 585-588.

*2.415  Weaver, D. K., "Design of RC Wide-Band 90 Degree Phase Difference Network," *Proc. IRE,* Vol. 42, April, 1954, pp. 671-676.

2.416  Storch, L., "Synthesis of Constant-Time Delay Ladder Networks Using Bessel Polynomials," *Proc. IRE,* Vol. 42, November, 1954, pp. 1666-1675.

2.417  Kuh, E. S., "Synthesis of Lumped Parameter Precision Delay Lines," *IRE Conv. Record,* Part 2, 1957, pp. 160-174.

2.418  Papoulis, A., "The Approximation Problem in Lumped Delay Lines," *IRE Conv. Record,* Part 2, 1958, pp. 102-108.

*2.419  Kulmann, C. A., "An Iterative Approximation to Flat Delay in an Equi-Ripple Manner," *ERL Report 89,* Univ. of California (Berkeley), June, 1959.

2.420  Szentirma, G., "The Problem of Phase Equalization," *Trans. IRE,* Vol. CT-6, September, 1959, pp. 272-277.

2.421  O'Meara, T. R., "Delay Distortion Correction for Networks and Filters," *IRE Wescon Conv. Record,* Part 2, 1960, pp. 123-134.

2.422  Golay, M., "Polynomials of Transfer Functions with Poles Satisfying Conditions Only at the Origin," *Trans. IRE,* Vol. CT-7, September, 1960, pp. 224-229.

*2.423 Piloty, H. and V. Ulbrich, "Uber den Entwurf von Allpassen, Tief-passen, und Bandpassen mit uner im Tschebyscheffschen approxi-mierton konstanten Gruppenlaufzeit," *Arch. Elek. Ubertragung*, Vol. 14, October, 1960, pp. 452-67.

2.424 O'Meara, T. R., "Linear-Slope Delay Filters for Compression," *Proc. IRE*, Vol. 48, November, 1960, pp. 1916-1918.

2.425 Uhl, K., "A Filter System with Favorable Impulse Properties," *Archiv der Elek. Ubertragung*, Vol. 15, No. 3, March, 1961, pp. 109-114.

2.426 Beletskiy, A. F., "Synthesis of Filters with Linear Phase Character-istics," *Telecommunications*, No. 4, April, 1961, pp. 39-48.

*2.427 Abele, T. A., "Ubertragungsfaktoren mit Tschebycheffscher Approxi-mation Konstanter Gruppenlaufzert," *Arch. Elek. Ubertragung*, Janu-ary, 1962, pp. 9-17.

2.428 Kirzrok, R. M., "A Technique for Equalizing Parabolic Group De-lay," *Proc. IRE*, Vol. 50, No. 8, August, 1962, p. 1840.

*2.429 Geffe, P. R., "On the Approximation Problem for Band-Pass Delay Lines," *Proc. IRE*, Vol. 50, No. 9, September, 1962, pp. 1986-1987.

*2.430 Humphreys, D. S., "Rational Function Approximation of Polynomials with Equi-Ripple Error," *Report No. R-159*, Coordinated Science Lab., University of Ill., February, 1963.

2.431 Macnee, A. B., "Tschebyscheff Approximation of a Constant Group Delay," 6th Midwest Symposium on Circuit Theory, Wisconsin, May, 1963.

## B2.5 Time Domain Approximation & Related Topics

2.501 Meerovich, L. A., "Network Synthesis According to a Given Transient Response Characteristic," *Radiotekhnika*, Vol. 3, 1948, pp. 36-42. (In Russian) (*See* Sci. Abs. B No. 1139 of 1949.)

2.502 Nadler, M., "The Synthesis of Electric Networks According to Pre-scribed Transient Conditions," *Proc. IRE*, Vol. 37, June, 1949, pp. 627-630.

2.503 Kautz, W. H., "Application of the Integral Approximation Method of Transient Evaluation," *Paper No. 30*, IRE *National Convention*, New York, N.Y., March 7, 1950.

2.504 Nadler, M., "A Note on the Synthesis of Electric Networks According to Prescribed Transient Response," *Proc. IRE*, Vol. 38, April, 1950, p. 441.

2.505 Kautz, W. H., "Network Synthesis for Specified Transient Response," *Tech. Rep. No. 209*, Res. Lab. for Elec., MIT, April 23, 1952. Also, *Paper No. 134, IRE National Conv.*, New York, N.Y., March, 1952.

2.506 Levy, M., "On the Redundant Information Supplied in Practical Applications in the Time and Frequency Phase Responses of a Sys-tem," *J. Appl. Phys.*, Vol. 23, July, 1952, pp. 801-802.

2.507 Linvill, W. K., "Use of Sampled Functions for Time Domain Syn-thesis," *Proc. NEC*, Vol. 9, 1953, pp. 533-542.

2.508  Thomson, W. E., "The Synthesis of a Network to Have a Sine-Squared Impulse Response," *Proc. IEE,* Vol. 99, Part III, November, 1952, pp. 373-376. Discussion, Vol. 100, 1953, p. 110.

2.509  Teasdale, R. D., "Time Domain Approximation by Use of Padé Approximants," *Convention Record IRE,* Part 5, Circuit Theory, March, 1953, pp. 89-94.

2.510  Wait, J. R., "An Approximate Method of Obtaining the Transient Response from the Frequency Response," *Can. J. Tech.,* Vol. 31, June, 1953, pp. 127-131.

2.511  Guillemin, E. A., "Computational Techniques Which Simplify the Correlations Between Steady-State and Transient Response of Filters and Other Networks," *Proc. NEC,* Vol. 9, 1953, pp. 513-523.

2.512  Fetzer, V., "On the Relation Between Time and Frequency Functions with Practical Examples of the Calculation of Transient Response of Linear Transmission Systems," *Arch. Elek. Ubertragung,* Vol. 8, April, 1954, pp. 163-177.

2.513  Zemanian, A. H., "Bounds Existing on the Time and Frequency Responses of Various Types of Networks," *Proc. IRE,* Vol. 42, May, 1954, pp. 835-839.

2.514  Covington, M. S., "Single Parameter Method for Relating Transient and Steady-State Response," *RCA Review,* Vol. 15, September, 1954, pp. 389-444.

2.515  Ba Hli, F., "A General Method of Time Domain Synthesis," *Trans. IRE,* Vol. CT-1, September, 1954.

2.516  Strieby, M., "A Fourier Method for Time Domain Synthesis," *Modern Network Synthesis,* MRI Symposium Series, Vol. V, 1955.

2.517  Zemanian, A. H., "Further Effects of the Pole and Zero Locations on the Step Responses of Fixed, Linear Systems," *Trans. AIEE,* Communications and Electronics, March, 1955, pp. 52-55.

2.518  Lang, G. R., "Time Domain Filter Operations," *Modern Network Synthesis,* MRI Symposium Series, Vol. V, 1955, pp. 267-282.

2.519  Rosenbrock, H. H., "An Approximate Method for Obtaining Transient Response from Frequency Response," *Proc. IRE,* Vol. 102, November, 1955, pp. 744-752.

2.520  Dawson, C. H., "Approximation of Transient Response from Frequency Response Data," *Trans. AIEE,* Applications and Industry, Part 2, Vol. 272, Nov., 1955, pp. 289-291.

2.521  Armstrong, H. L., "On Finding an Orthonormal Basis for Representing Transients," *Trans. IRE,* Vol. CT-4, September, 1957, p. 286.

2.522  Brode, J. D., "Improving the Approximation to a Prescribed Time Response," *Trans. IRE,* Vol. CT-6, December, 1957, pp. 355-361.

2.523  Henderson, K. W. and W. H. Kautz, "Transient Response of Conventional Filters," *Trans. IRE,* Vol. CT-5, December, 1958.

2.524  Graham, J. D., "An Approximation of Transient Response from Frequency Response Data," *Proc. IRE,* April, 1959, p. 591.

2.525 Levadi, V. S., "Simplified Method of Determining Transient Response from Frequency Response of Linear Networks and Systems," *IRE Conv. Rec.*, Part 4, 1959, p. 57.

2.526 Tang, D. T., "Tchebycheff Approximation of a Prescribed Impulse Response with RC Network Realization," *IRE Conv. Rec.*, Part 4, 1961, pp. 214-220.

2.527 Yengst, W. C., "Approximation to a Specified Time Response," *Trans. IRE,* Vol. CT-9, No. 2, June, 1962, pp. 152-162.

2.528. Liu, B., "A Time Domain Approximation Method and Its Application to Lumped Delay Lines," *Trans. IRE,* Vol. CT-9, September, 1962.

## B2.6 *Potential Analogy*

2.601 Kenyon, R. W., "Network Design Using Electrolytic Tanks," *Elec. Ind.,* Vol. 5, March, 1946, pp. 58-60.

2.602 Huggins, W. H., "A Note on Frequency Transformations for Use with the Electrolytic Tank," *Proc. IRE.,* Vol. 36, March, 1948, pp. 421-424.

2.603 Makar, R., A. R. Boothroyd and E. C. Cherry, "An Electrolytic Tank for Exploring Potential Field Distributions," *Nature,* Vol. 161, May 29, 1948, pp. 845-846.

2.604 Block, A., "Solution of Algebraic Equations by Means of an Electrolytic Tank," *Paper No. IV-28, VII International Congress App. Mech.,* London, 1948.

2.605 Boothroyd, A. R., E. C. Cherry and R. Makar, "An Electrolytic Tank for the Measurement of Steady State Response, Transient Response, and Allied Properties of Networks," *Journal IEE,* Part 1, Vol. 96, May, 1949, pp. 163-177.

2.606 Huggins, W. H., "The Potential Analogue in Network Synthesis and Analysis," *Rep. 5066,* Air Force Res. Labs., Cambridge, Mass., March, 1951.

2.607 Darlington, S., "The Potential Analogue of Network Synthesis," *BSTJ,* Vol. 30, April, 1951, pp. 315-365.

2.608 Boothroyd, A. R., "Design of Electric Wave Filters with the Aid of the Electrolytic Tank," *Proc. IEE,* Part IV, Vol. 98, October, 1951, pp. 65-93. Summary, Part III, Vol. 98, November, 1951, pp. 486-492.

2.609 Cherry, E. C., "Application of the Electrolytic Tank Techniques to Network Synthesis," *Modern Network Synthesis,* MRI Symposium Series, Vol. II, April, 1952, pp. 140-159.

2.610 Scott, R. E., "Network Synthesis By the Use of Potential Analogs," *Proc. IRE,* Vol. 40, No. 8, August, 1952.

2.611 Kuh, E. S., "Potential Analog-Network Synthesis for Arbitrary Loss Functions," *Journal App. Phys.,* Vol. 24, July, 1953, pp. 897-902.

B2.7 *Related Topics—Pertaining to Ladder Realization*
(See, also, Section 82.2)

2.701 Darlington, S., "Synthesis of Reactance Four-Poles," *Jour. Math. and Physics,* Vol. 18, 1939, pp. 247-353.

2.702 Colombe, P., "Rational Calculation of Ladder-Type Filters," *Bull. Soc. Franc. Elect.,* Vol. 6, March, 1946, pp. 103-110.

2.703 Dishal, M., "Design of Dissipative Band-Pass Filters Producing Desired Exact Amplitude Frequency Characteristics," *Proc. IRE,* Vol. 37, September, 1949, pp. 1050-1069.

2.704 Belevitch, V., "Tchebycheff Filters and Amplifier Networks," *Wireless Eng.,* Vol. 29, April, 1952, pp. 106-110.

2.705 Fetzer, V., "Numerical Calculation of Filter Circuits with Tchebycheff Characteristics after the Method of W. Cauer," *Arch. Elek. Ubertragung,* Vol. 6, October, 1952, pp. 419-431.

2.706 Orchard, H. J., "Formulae for Ladder Filters," *Wireless Engrg.,* Vol. 30, January, 1953, pp. 3-5.

2.707 Fetzer, V., "Practical Calculation of Jacobi 'sn' Elliptic Function with Special Reference to the Determination of the Cauer Parameter for Filters with Operative Attenuation Characteristics," *Arch. Elek. Ubertragung.,* Vol. 7, August, 1953, pp. 393-401.

2.708 Green, E., "Synthesis of Ladder Networks to Give Butterworth or Chebychev Response in the Pass Band," *IEE Monograph 88,* January 15, 1954.

*2.709 Fugisawa, T., "Realizability Theorem for Mid-Series or Mid-Shunt Low-Pass Ladders Without Mutual Induction," *Trans. IRE,* Vol. CT-2 No. 4, December, 1955, pp. 320-325.

2.710 Peless, Y. and T. Murakami, "Analysis and Synthesis of Transitional Butterworth-Thomson Filters and Bandpass Amplifiers," *RCA Review,* Vol. 18, No. 1, March, 1957, pp. 60-94.

2.711 Grossman, A., "Synthesis of Tchebycheff Parameter Symmetrical Filters," *Proc. IRE,* Vol. 45, No. 4, April, 1957, p. 454.

2.712 Baum, R. F., "Design of Unsymmetrical Bandpass Filters," *Trans. IRE,* Vol. CT-4, June, 1957, pp. 33-40.

*2.713 Desoer, C. A., "Network Design by First Order Predistortion Technique," *Trans. IRE,* Vol. CT-4, September, 1957, pp. 167-170.

*2.714 Weinberg, L., "Exact Ladder Network Design Using Low Q Coils," *Proc. IRE,* April, 1958, p. 739.

2.715 Orchard, H. J., "Computation of Elliptic Functions of Rational Fractions of a Quarterperiod," *Trans. IRE,* Vol. CT-5, December, 1958, pp. 352-355.

2.716 Skivirzynski, J. K. and J. Zdunek, "Note on Calculation of Ladder Coefficients for Symmetrical and Inverse Impedance Filters on a Digital Computer," *Trans. IRE,* Vol. CT-5, December, 1958, pp. 328-333.

*2.717 Saal, R. and E. Ulbrich, "On the Design of Filters by. Synthesis," *Trans. IRE,* Vol. CT-5, December, 1958, pp. 284-327.

APPENDIX II: BIBLIOGRAPHY

**97**

2.718 Meinguet, J. and V. Belevitch, "On the Realizability of Ladder Filters," *Trans. IRE,* Vol. CT-5, No. 4, December, 1958, pp. 253-255.

2.719 Henderson, R. W. and W. H. Kantz, "Transient Responses of Conventional Filters," *Trans. IRE,* Vol. CT-5, No. 4, December, 1958, pp. 333-347.

*2.720 Geffe, P. R., "A Note on Predistortion," *Trans. IRE,* Vol. CT-6, December, 1959, p. 395.

2.721 Pawsey, D. C., "Element Coefficients for Symmetrical Two-Section Filters Having Tchebycheff Response in Both Pass and Stop Bands," *Trans. IRE,* Vol. CT-7, No. 1, March, 1960, pp. 19-31.

*2.772 Orchard, H. J., "Predistortion of Singly-Loaded Reactance Networks," *Trans. IRE,* Vol. CT-7, No. 2, June, 1960, pp. 181-182.

2.723 Weinberg, L. and P. Stepian, "Takahasi's Results on Tchebycheff and Butterworth Ladder Networks," *Trans. IRE,* Vol. CT-7, No. 2, June, 1960, pp. 88-101.

*2.724 Saal, V. R., "Der Entwurf von Filtern mit Hilfe des Kataloges normiester Tiefpasse," 1961. (A catalog of element values for elliptic filters can be ordered for $2.50 from Telefunken Co., Backnang/Wurtt, Western Germany.)

2.725 Bedrosian, S. D., "Elliptic Functions in Network Synthesis," *J. Franklin Inst.,* Vol. 271, No. 1, January, 1961, pp. 12-30.

2.726 Leviman, G. I., and O. I. Vostryakov, "Synthesis of Polynomial Bandpass Filters with Chebyshev Selectivity Characteristic," *Telecommunications,* No. 2, February, 1961, pp. 66-80.

*2.727 Bosse, G., "The Calculation of the Numerical Values of Elliptic Functions for Tchebycheff Filters," *Frequency,* Vol. 15, No. 8, August, 1961, pp. 249-253.

*2.728 Tollefsrud, V. C., "A New Computational Method for Predistortion," *Trans. IRE,* Vol. CT-9, March, 1962, pp. 92-93.

2.729 Szentirma, G., "On the Realizability of Ladder Filters," *Trans. IRE,* Vol. CT-9, March, 1962, pp 91-92.

*2.730 Geffe, P. R., and H. J. Orchard, "A Further Note on Predistortion," *Trans. IRE,* Vol. CT-9, No. 3, September, 1962, pp. 291-292.

*2.731 Temes, G. C., "First-Order Estimation and Precorrection of Parasitic Loss Effects in Ladder Filters," *Trans. IRE,* Vol. CT-9, No. 4, December, 1962, pp. 385-399.

*2.732 Geffe, P. R., *Simplified Modern Filter Design.* New York, N.Y.: John F. Rider Publisher, Inc., 1963.

# INDEX